THE GIANT
JEOPARDY!™
QUIZ BOOK

D1316708

THE GIANT
JEOPARDY!
QUIZ BOOK

Jeopardy! . . . What Is Quiz Book 3?
Jeopardy! . . . What Is Quiz Book 4?

Quality Paperback Book Club
New York

The Giant Jeopardy Quiz Book

Jeopardy! . . . What Is Quiz Book 3?
Copyright © 2000 by Jeopardy Productions, Inc.

Jeopardy! . . . What Is Quiz Book 4?
Copyright © 2000 by Jeopardy Productions, Inc.

All rights reserved. No part of this book may be used or reproduced in any manner whatsoever without written permission except in the case of reprints in the context of reviews. For information, write Andrews McMeel Publishing, an Andrews McMeel Universal company, 4520 Main Street, Kansas City, Missouri 64111.

Jeopardy! is a trademark of Jeopardy Productions, Inc. TM and © 2001 Jeopardy Productions, Inc. All rights reserved.

This edition was especially created in 2001 for Quality Paperback Book Club by arrangement with Andrews McMeel Publishing.

Printed in the United States of America

JEOPARDY!™

What Is Quiz Book 3?

JEOPARDY!

FOOD & DRINK

BY DEFINITION, A SANDWICH THAT IS OPEN-FACED LACKS THIS ON TOP	**$100**	WHAT IS
THIS BASIC SAUCE NAMED FOR ITS COLOR IS OFTEN THE FOUNDATION OF CHEESE SAUCE	**$200**	WHAT IS
OFTEN SERVED WITH FRUIT FOR DESSERT, TALEGGIO IS A CHEESE FROM THIS COUNTRY	**$300**	WHAT IS
YOU CAN ADD A DE-LIGHTFULLY WOODSY FLAVOR TO YOUR ENTREES WITH PORCINI, A TYPE OF THESE	**$400**	WHAT ARE
"FORMOSA" OFTEN PRECEDES THE NAME OF THIS TEA WHOSE NAME COMES FROM THE CHINESE FOR "BLACK DRAGON"	**$500**	WHAT IS

JEOPARDY!

FOOD & DRINK

$100	WHAT IS BREAD?	**$100**
$200	WHAT IS WHITE SAUCE?	**$200**
$300	WHAT IS ITALY?	**$300**
$400	WHAT ARE MUSHROOMS?	**$400**
$500	WHAT IS OOLONG?	**$500**

JEOPARDY!

BIOGRAPHIES

MERLE MILLER'S 1980 BOOK "LYNDON" IS "AN ORAL BIOGRAPHY" OF THIS MAN	**$100**	WHO IS
A 1991 BOOK ABOUT THIS ACTOR, JFK'S BROTHER-IN-LAW, IS SUBTITLED "THE MAN WHO KEPT THE SECRETS"	**$200**	WHO IS
LOUIS HARLAN'S BIOGRAPHY OF THIS TUSKEGEE EDUCATOR WON A 1984 PULITZER PRIZE	**$300**	WHO IS
THE TABLES WERE TURNED ON THIS BIOG-RAPHER WHEN SHE BECAME THE SUBJECT OF THE UNAUTHORIZED BOOK "POISON PEN"	**$400**	WHO IS
"THE MAN WHO PRESUMED" TELLS THE STORY OF THIS EXPLORER	**$500**	WHO IS

JEOPARDY!

BIOGRAPHIES

$100   WHO IS LYNDON JOHNSON? $100

$200   WHO IS PETER LAWFORD? $200

$300   WHO IS BOOKER T. WASHINGTON? $300

$400   WHO IS KITTY KELLEY? $400

$500   WHO IS HENRY STANLEY? $500

4

JEOPARDY!

THE MOVIES

THIS 1964 PETER SELLERS TITLE CHARACTER IS A MAD GERMAN SCIENTIST	**$100**	WHO IS
THIS "ER" HUNK WAS AFTER SADDAM'S GOLD IN "THREE KINGS"	**$200**	WHO IS
CHRISTOPHER ATKINS LEARNS ABOUT THE BIRDS & THE BEES ON A DESERT ISLAND WITH THIS ACTRESS IN "THE BLUE LAGOON"	**$300**	WHO IS
"CAN'T HARDLY WAIT", ABOUT A BLOW-OUT HIGH SCHOOL GRADUATION PARTY, STARRED THIS "PARTY OF FIVE" ACTRESS	**$400**	WHO IS
JUDITH GUEST'S NOVEL ABOUT A DYSFUNC-TIONAL FAMILY BECAME THIS 1980 MOVIE WITH MARY TYLER MOORE & TIMOTHY HUTTON	**$500**	WHAT IS

JEOPARDY!

THE MOVIES

$100 WHO IS DR. STRANGELOVE? **$100**

$200 WHO IS GEORGE CLOONEY? **$200**

$300 WHO IS BROOKE SHIELDS? **$300**

$400 WHO IS JENNIFER LOVE HEWITT? **$400**

$500 WHAT IS "ORDINARY PEOPLE"? **$500**

JEOPARDY!

AMERICAN HISTORY

IN 1833 THIS AREA ASKED TO SEPARATE FROM COAHUILA TO BECOME ITS OWN MEXICAN STATE	**$100**	WHAT IS
IN 1901 BUFFALO BILL FOUNDED THIS TOWN IN THE BIG HORN BASIN OF WYOMING	**$200**	WHAT IS
FRANCES WILLARD, A PRESIDENT OF THE WCTU, WAS THE FIRST WOMAN HONORED IN THIS CAPITOL BUILDING HALL	**$300**	WHAT IS
IN AUGUST 1999 PRESIDENT CLINTON OFFERED CLEMENCY TO 16 TERRORISTS FROM THIS ISLAND	**$400**	WHAT IS
THE CHANGE IN THE AMERICAN FLAG ON JULY 4, 1960 WAS ITS FIRST CHANGE SINCE JULY 4 OF THIS YEAR	**$500**	WHAT IS

JEOPARDY!

AMERICAN HISTORY

$100	WHAT IS TEXAS?	**$100**
$200	WHAT IS CODY?	**$200**
$300	WHAT IS (NATIONAL) STATUARY HALL?	**$300**
$400	WHAT IS PUERTO RICO?	**$400**
$500	WHAT IS 1959?	**$500**

JEOPARDY!

NUTRITION

Clue	Value	Response
THIS "SUNSHINE VITAMIN" IS UNIQUE IN THAT IT FUNCTIONS NOT ONLY AS A VITAMIN BUT ALSO AS A HORMONE	$100	WHAT IS
FOR PROPER COLON HEALTH, IT'S BEEN SUGGESTED YOU GET 20–35 GRAMS PER DAY OF THIS, BOTH SOLUBLE & INSOLUBLE FORMS	$200	WHAT IS
ABOUT 70% OF THE IRON WE ABSORB ENDS UP IN THIS PROTEIN IN RED BLOOD CELLS	$300	WHAT IS
MUSCLE SPASMS & LEG CRAMPS CAN BE PREVENTED WITH ADEQUATE AMOUNTS OF THIS MINERAL, SYMBOL Mg	$400	WHAT IS
A GOOD ANTIOXIDANT, IT'S ALSO CALLED TOCOPHEROL	$500	WHAT IS

JEOPARDY!

NUTRITION

$100	WHAT IS VITAMIN D?	**$100**
$200	WHAT IS FIBER?	**$200**
$300	WHAT IS THE HEMOGLOBIN?	**$300**
$400	WHAT IS MAGNESIUM?	**$400**
$500	WHAT IS VITAMIN E?	**$500**

JEOPARDY!

THE "IN" SOUND

THE SOUTH AMERICAN EMPIRE OF THESE PEOPLE INCLUDED PARTS OF PRESENT-DAY ECUADOR, PERU, CHILE & ARGENTINA	**$100**	WHO ARE
FROM THE LATIN FOR "TO SET ON FIRE", IT'S AN AROMATIC SUBSTANCE BURNED TO PRODUCE A PLEASANT ODOR	**$200**	WHAT IS
THE MAIN ISLANDS OF THIS COUNTRY INCLUDE BORNEO, SULAWESI, JAVA & SUMATRA	**$300**	WHAT IS
USUALLY THE LARGEST BRANCH OF AN ARMY, IT'S ANOTHER NAME FOR FOOT SOLDIERS	**$400**	WHAT IS
A FURNACE-LIKE DEVICE FOR REDUCING WASTE PRODUCTS TO ASH	**$500**	WHAT IS

JEOPARDY!

THE "IN" SOUND

$100   WHO ARE THE INCAS? $100

$200   WHAT IS INCENSE? $200

$300   WHAT IS INDONESIA? $300

$400   WHAT IS THE INFANTRY? $400

$500   WHAT IS AN INCINERATOR? $500

DOUBLE JEOPARDY!

ISLAND COUNTRIES

ON OCT. 22, 1962 PRESIDENT KENNEDY REVEALED THAT RUSSIA HAD BUILT MISSILE BASES IN THIS COUNTRY	**$200**	WHAT IS
THE FIRST PERMANENT SETTLER IN THIS COUNTRY WAS A NORWEGIAN VIKING NAMED INGÓLFUR ARNARSON	**$400**	WHAT IS
NICOSIA & LIMASSOL ARE THE ONLY 2 CITIES WITH A POPULATION OF OVER 100,000 IN THIS COUNTRY	**$600**	WHAT IS
WE'RE NOT PULLING THE WOOL OVER YOUR EYES WHEN WE TELL YOU IT WAS THE FIRST NATION TO GRANT WOMEN THE RIGHT TO VOTE	**$800**	WHAT IS
IN AREA, IT'S THE LARGER OF THE 2 COUNTRIES THAT OCCUPY HISPANIOLA	**$1000**	WHAT IS

DOUBLE JEOPARDY!

ISLAND COUNTRIES

$200   WHAT IS CUBA?   **$200**

$400   WHAT IS ICELAND?   **$400**

$600   WHAT IS CYPRUS?   **$600**

$800   WHAT IS NEW ZEALAND?   **$800**

$1000   WHAT IS THE DOMINICAN REPUBLIC?   **$1000**

DOUBLE JEOPARDY!

5-LETTER WORDS

MEANING ELEGANT OR FANCY, IT'S FROM THE NAME OF A HOTEL CHAIN	**$200**	WHAT IS
IT CAN PRECEDE COMB, SUCKLE & MOON	**$400**	WHAT IS
THE NAME OF THIS HOODED FUR JACKET IS PROBABLY DERIVED FROM THE RUSSIAN FOR "PELT"	**$600**	WHAT IS
"THE STAR-SPANGLED BANNER" ENDS WITH THIS "VALIANT" WORD	**$800**	WHAT IS
AS A VERB, IT MEANS TO ADD TERRITORY TO AN EXISTING COUNTRY; AS A NOUN, IT'S A BUILDING ADDED TO A LARGER ONE	**$1000**	WHAT IS

DOUBLE JEOPARDY!

5-LETTER WORDS

$200 — WHAT IS RITZY? — $200

$400 — WHAT IS HONEY? — $400

$600 — WHAT IS PARKA? — $600

$800 — WHAT IS BRAVE? — $800

$1000 — WHAT IS ANNEX? — $1000

DOUBLE JEOPARDY!

LADIES OF LITERATURE

URSULA & HER SISTER GUDRUN ARE THE TITLE "WOMEN" OF THIS D.H. LAWRENCE NOVEL	**$200**	WHAT IS
IN "THE SCARLET LETTER", THE RESULT OF HER "A"DULTERY IS HER BEAUTIFUL DAUGHTER PEARL	**$400**	WHO IS
IN WILLIAM STYRON'S BOOK HER "CHOICE" IS WHICH OF HER CHILDREN IS SENT TO DEATH	**$600**	WHO IS
THE CLASSIC NOVEL "ULYSSES" ENDS WITH A 50-PAGE MONOLOGUE BY THIS SECOND-RATE DUBLIN SINGER	**$800**	WHO IS
IN 1878 HENRY JAMES' "FLOWERY" PROSE TOLD OF THIS SCHENECTADY GIRL TRAVELING IN EUROPE	**$1000**	WHO IS

DOUBLE JEOPARDY!

LADIES OF LITERATURE

$200 | WHAT IS "WOMEN IN LOVE"? | $200

$400 | WHO IS HESTER PRYNNE? | $400

$600 | WHO IS SOPHIE (ZAWISTOWSKA)? | $600

$800 | WHO IS MOLLY BLOOM? | $800

$1000 | WHO IS DAISY MILLER? | $1000

DOUBLE JEOPARDY!

YOU AUTO KNOW

SQUEEZE THESE RADIATOR ATTACHMENTS & REPLACE THEM IF THEY'RE GOING SOFT ON YOU	**$200**	WHAT ARE
THE ONE USED TO CHECK POWER STEERING FLUID IS SHORTER THAN THE ONE USED TO CHECK ENGINE OIL	**$400**	WHAT IS
LIKE A COMEDIAN, A CAR OWNER MAY NEED TO "ADJUST" THIS, PERHAPS BY ADVANCING THE SPARK	**$600**	WHAT IS
ALSO THE NAME OF A COMIC STRIP, IT MAKES THE PISTONS' UP-&-DOWN MOTION CIRCULAR	**$800**	WHAT IS
THROTTLE-BODY & MULTIPORT ARE THE 2 MAIN TYPES OF THIS SYSTEM OF DELIVERING GAS TO THE ENGINE	**$1000**	WHAT IS

DOUBLE JEOPARDY!

YOU AUTO KNOW

$200 — WHAT ARE THE HOSES? — $200

$400 — WHAT IS A DIPSTICK? — $400

$600 — WHAT IS THE TIMING? — $600

$800 — WHAT IS THE CRANKSHAFT? — $800

$1000 — WHAT IS FUEL INJECTION? — $1000

DOUBLE JEOPARDY!

1960s POP MUSIC

DRUMMER ANDY WHITE PLAYED ON THIS GROUP'S U.S. RELEASE OF "LOVE ME DO"	**$200**	WHAT IS
HE FOLLOWED "THE TWIST" WITH "LET'S TWIST AGAIN" & "SLOW TWISTIN'"	**$400**	WHO IS
"BIG BAD" MAN FEATURED IN A JIMMY DEAN HIT	**$600**	WHO IS
INSTRUMENT PLAYED BY STEVIE WONDER ON HIS 1963 HIT "FINGERTIPS (PART 2)"	**$800**	WHAT IS
IN DECEMBER 1963 THIS HIT BY THE SINGING NUN RAPIDLY CLIMBED THE CHARTS & REMAINED NO. 1 FOR THE ENTIRE MONTH	**$1000**	WHAT IS

DOUBLE JEOPARDY!

1960s POP MUSIC

$200	WHAT IS THE BEATLES?	**$200**
$400	WHO IS CHUBBY CHECKER?	**$400**
$600	WHO IS "BIG BAD JOHN"?	**$600**
$800	WHAT IS THE HARMONICA?	**$800**
$1000	WHAT IS "DOMINIQUE"?	**$1000**

DOUBLE JEOPARDY!

THE CORNER DRUGSTORE

Clue		Response
ERGOTAMINE, INTRODUCED IN THE 1920s, HELPS CONTROL THE MIGRAINE & VASCULAR TYPES OF THESE	$200	WHAT ARE
BEST-KNOWN BRAND NAME OF DIAZEPAM, AN ANTI-ANXIETY DRUG INTRODUCED IN 1963	$400	WHAT IS
AVAILABLE AS A LIQUID & A TABLET, IT MAAKES THE CLAIM "NO. 1 HEARTBURN BRAND IN HOSPITALS"	$600	WHAT IS
THIS "COLORFUL" HERB, HYDRASTIS CANADENSIS, IS COMBINED WITH ECHINACEA TO BOOST THE IMMUNE SYSTEM	$800	WHAT IS
KIDS' PRESCRIPTIONS FOR THIS DRUG, ALSO CALLED METHYLPHENIDATE, "A.D.D." UP TO A 700% INCREASE IN THE '90s	$1000	WHAT IS

DOUBLE JEOPARDY!

THE CORNER DRUGSTORE

$200	WHAT ARE HEADACHES?	**$200**
$400	WHAT IS VALIUM?	**$400**
$600	WHAT IS MAALOX?	**$600**
$800	WHAT IS GOLDENSEAL?	**$800**
$1000	WHAT IS RITALIN?	**$1000**

FINAL JEOPARDY!

20th CENTURY LEADERS

THIS DICTATOR BUILT THE
VALLEY OF THE FALLEN, HIS
FINAL RESTING PLACE, JUST
NORTH OF EL ESCORIAL

WHO IS

FINAL JEOPARDY!

20th CENTURY LEADERS

WHO IS FRANCISCO
FRANCO?

JEOPARDY!

HISTORIC AMOURS

WHEN THIS "OLIVER TWIST" AUTHOR FELL FOR AN ACTRESS HIS WIFE TWISTED HIS ARM FOR A LEGAL SEPARATION	**$100**	WHO IS
HE PREFERRED THE "BOUNTY"OUS BEAUTY OF MAUATUA TO BLIGH & BREADFRUIT	**$200**	WHO IS
IT'S LIKELY THAT ETTA PLACE, THE COMPANION OF THIS "KID", WAS A LADY OF THE EVENING RATHER THAN A SCHOOLMARM	**$300**	WHO IS
ACTRESS NELL GWYN WAS THE LOVER OF LORD BUCKHURST BEFORE SHE CAUGHT THE EYE OF THIS "MERRY MONARCH"	**$400**	WHO IS
LOUIS I's LUST FOR LOLA MONTEZ LED HIM TO LOSE THE THRONE OF THIS GERMAN KINGDOM	**$500**	WHAT IS

JEOPARDY!™

HISTORIC AMOURS

$100	WHO IS CHARLES DICKENS?	**$100**
$200	WHO IS FLETCHER CHRISTIAN?	**$200**
$300	WHO IS THE SUNDANCE KID?	**$300**
$400	WHO IS CHARLES II?	**$400**
$500	WHAT IS BAVARIA?	**$500**

JEOPARDY!

U.S. GEOGRAPHY

Clue	Value	Response
THIS RIVER'S DELTA COVERS MORE THAN 12,000 SQUARE MILES IN LOUISIANA	$100	WHAT IS
THE WICHITA MOUNTAINS ARE NOT IN KANSAS BUT IN THIS STATE ON ITS SOUTHERN BORDER	$200	WHAT IS
ALTHOUGH A MILE WIDE IN SOME PLACES, THIS PRINCIPAL RIVER OF NEBRASKA IS TOO SHALLOW TO BE NAVIGABLE	$300	WHAT IS
THIS STATE CAPITAL IS KNOWN FOR A VARIETY OF OYSTERS FOUND PRIMARILY IN PUGET SOUND	$400	WHAT IS
A PARKWAY NAMED FOR THESE MOUNTAINS LINKS SHENANDOAH & GREAT SMOKY MOUNTAINS NATIONAL PARKS	$500	WHAT ARE

29

JEOPARDY!

U.S. GEOGRAPHY

$100
WHAT IS THE
MISSISSIPPI RIVER?
$100

$200
WHAT IS OKLAHOMA?
$200

$300
WHAT IS THE
PLATTE RIVER?
$300

$400
WHAT IS OLYMPIA?
$400

$500
WHAT ARE THE BLUE
RIDGE MOUNTAINS?
$500

JEOPARDY!

SITCOMS

ON THIS SITCOM IN 1998, TIM TAYLOR'S SON RANDY RAN OFF TO WORK IN A COSTA RICAN RAINFOREST	**$100**	WHAT IS
ON HER SELF-TITLED SITCOM, SHE WORKED AT A PLASTICS FACTORY & A BEAUTY SALON BEFORE OPENING HER OWN DINER	**$200**	WHO IS
ENRICO COLANTONI PLAYS A PHOTOGRA-PHER & LAURA SAN GIACOMO A JOURN-ALIST ON THIS SHOW	**$300**	WHAT IS
ON THE WB SHOW NAMED FOR THIS COMIC, HE LIVES AT HIS FAMILY'S HOTEL WHILE STRIVING FOR STARDOM	**$400**	WHO IS
HER FIRST PRIMETIME ROLE WAS ON "KATE & ALLIE"; NOW SHE PLAYS KATE ON THE "THE DREW CAREY SHOW"	**$500**	WHO IS

31

JEOPARDY!

SITCOMS

$100 WHAT IS "HOME IMPROVEMENT"? **$100**

$200 WHO IS ROSEANNE? **$200**

$300 WHAT IS "JUST SHOOT ME"? **$300**

$400 WHO IS JAMIE FOXX? **$400**

$500 WHO IS CHRISTA MILLER? **$500**

JEOPARDY!

TECHNOLOGY

SUGGESTIONS ON WHAT TO CALL THIS DEVICE RANGED FROM FARSCOPE TO TELEBAIRD	**$100**	WHAT IS
HUBERT BOOTH, NOT HERBERT HOOVER, DEVELOPED THE FIRST PRACTICAL ELECTRIC ONE OF THESE IN 1901	**$200**	WHAT IS
IN 1982 ONE OF THESE VEHICLES DEPLOYED A SATELLITE FOR THE FIRST TIME	**$300**	WHAT IS
UNTIL A 1967 TABLE TOP MODEL WITH A SMALLER ELECTRON TUBE WAS INTRODUCED, THIS KITCHEN DEVICE WAS BIG & PRICEY	**$400**	WHAT IS
ON AUGUST 12, 1981 THE WORLD SAW THE FIRST IBM PERSONAL COMPUTER USING THIS MICROSOFT OPERATING SYSTEM	**$500**	WHAT IS

JEOPARDY!

TECHNOLOGY

$100	WHAT IS THE TELEVISION?	$100
$200	WHAT IS A VACUUM CLEANER?	$200
$300	WHAT IS A SPACE SHUTTLE?	$300
$400	WHAT IS A MICROWAVE OVEN?	$400
$500	WHAT IS MS-DOS?	$500

JEOPARDY!™

"OLD" GLORY

A NURSERY RHYME'S "MERRY OLD SOUL"	**$100**	WHO IS
A PBS SERIES ONCE HOSTED BY BOB VILA	**$200**	WHAT IS
A 1952 HEMINGWAY NOVELLA	**$300**	WHAT IS
GENERAL GEORGE PATTON'S VISCERAL NICKNAME	**$400**	WHAT IS
ALSO THE TITLE OF A 1595 PLAY, IT'S A TRADITIONAL BELIEF OR STORY THAT'S OFTEN SUPERSTITIOUS	**$500**	WHAT IS

JEOPARDY!™

"OLD" GLORY

$100 | WHO IS OLD KING COLE? | **$100**

$200 | WHAT IS "THIS OLD HOUSE"? | **$200**

$300 | WHAT IS "THE OLD MAN AND THE SEA"? | **$300**

$400 | WHAT IS "OLD BLOOD AND GUTS"? | **$400**

$500 | WHAT IS AN OLD WIVES' TALE? | **$500**

JEOPARDY!

LITTLE-READ BOOKS

THIS EARLY SCI-FI WRITER TACKLED POLAR EXPLORATION (FROM HIS STUDY) IN THE 1860s WITH "AVENTURES DU CAPITAINE HATTERAS"	**$100**	WHO IS
YOU MIGHT HAVE TO BE ON A DESERT ISLAND BEFORE YOU GET AROUND TO HIS 1722 NOVEL "COLONEL JACK"	**$200**	WHO IS
THIS AUTHOR OF "AN AMERICAN TRAGEDY" ALSO WROTE A LITTLE-READ TREATISE CALLED "TRAGIC AMERICA"	**$300**	WHO IS
MANY READERS DON'T GET THROUGH THE SLOUGH OF DESPOND IN THIS 1678 JOHN BUNYAN WORK	**$400**	WHAT IS
KANT STRAINED BRAINS WITH THIS TYPE OF ANALYSIS "OF PURE REASON" & "OF JUDGMENT"	**$500**	WHAT IS

37

JEOPARDY!

LITTLE-READ BOOKS

$100	WHO IS JULES VERNE?
$200	WHO IS DANIEL DEFOE?
$300	WHO IS THEODORE DREISER?
$400	WHAT IS "THE PILGRIM'S PROGRESS"?
$500	WHAT IS A CRITIQUE?

DOUBLE JEOPARDY!

HUMANITARIANS

Clue	Value	Response
HER PARENTS ASKED ALEXANDER GRAHAM BELL ABOUT A TEACHER FOR THEIR DAUGHTER; ANNE SULLIVAN WAS SOON HIRED	**$200**	WHO IS
HE USED SOME OF HIS ENORMOUS WEALTH TO BUILD A NEW YORK CITY CONCERT HALL & OVER 2,500 PUBLIC LIBRARIES	**$400**	WHO IS
IN 1931 THIS SOCIAL REFORMER & HULL HOUSE FOUNDER WAS A CO-WINNER OF THE NOBEL PEACE PRIZE	**$600**	WHO IS
BILLIONAIRE KIRK KERKORIAN HAS PROVIDED $100 MILLION FOR AN AIRLIFT TO THIS COUNTRY	**$800**	WHAT IS
HE BEGAN STUDYING YELLOW FEVER IN 1897, 3 YEARS PRIOR TO BEING APPOINTED TO A COMMISSION TO FIND ITS CAUSE	**$1000**	WHO IS

DOUBLE JEOPARDY!

HUMANITARIANS

$200	WHO IS HELEN KELLER?	**$200**
$400	WHO IS ANDREW CARNEGIE?	**$400**
$600	WHO IS JANE ADDAMS?	**$600**
$800	WHAT IS ARMENIA?	**$800**
$1000	WHO IS DR. WALTER REED?	**$1000**

DOUBLE JEOPARDY!

TOUGH SHAKESPEARE

ON AN EPISODE OF THE TV SHOW "MOON-LIGHTING", CYBILL SHEPHERD WAS KATE IN AN ADAPTATION OF THIS PLAY	**$200**	WHAT IS
IN THIS COMEDY'S SUBPLOT, SIR TOBY BELCH & MARIA PLAY A TRICK ON MALVOLIO, OLIVIA'S STEWARD	**$400**	WHAT IS
PURSUED BY DEMETRIUS & HELENA, HERMIA & LYSANDER ELOPE TO A WOOD NEAR ATHENS IN THIS COMEDY	**$600**	WHAT IS
COMPLETES SONNET 130's FIRST LINE, "MY MISTRESS' EYES ARE . . ."	**$800**	WHAT IS
IN "KING LEAR" THE EARL OF GLOUCESTER BOASTS OF THIS BASTARD SON: "THERE WAS GOOD SPORT AT HIS MAKING"	**$1000**	WHO IS

DOUBLE JEOPARDY!

TOUGH SHAKESPEARE

$200	WHAT IS "THE TAMING OF THE SHREW"?	**$200**
$400	WHAT IS "TWELFTH NIGHT (OR, WHAT YOU WILL)"?	**$400**
$600	WHAT IS "A MID-SUMMER NIGHT'S DREAM"?	**$600**
$800	WHAT IS "NOTHING LIKE THE SUN"?	**$800**
$1000	WHO IS EDMUND?	**$1000**

DOUBLE JEOPARDY!

PLAY BALL!

Clue	Value	Response
THIS EVENT, WHICH HAPPENED MINUTES BEFORE THE START OF GAME 3 IN 1989, POSTPONED THE WORLD SERIES FOR 10 DAYS	$200	WHAT IS
IN 1941 THIS RED SOX OUTFIELDER HIT A SPECTACULAR .406	$400	WHO IS
HALL OF FAMER ROBERTO CLEMENTE SPENT HIS ENTIRE 18-YEAR MAJOR LEAGUE CAREER WITH THIS TEAM	$600	WHAT ARE
NICKNAME OF ALL-STAR THIRD BASEMAN LARRY JONES	$800	WHAT IS
THIS CINCINNATI REDS PLAYER APPEARED IN 3,562 GAMES, THE MOST BY ANY PLAYER IN MAJOR LEAGUE HISTORY	$1000	WHO IS

DOUBLE JEOPARDY!

PLAY BALL!

$200	WHAT IS AN EARTHQUAKE?	**$200**
$400	WHO IS TED WILLIAMS?	**$400**
$600	WHAT ARE THE PITTSBURGH PIRATES?	**$600**
$800	WHAT IS CHIPPER?	**$800**
$1000	WHO IS PETE ROSE?	**$1000**

DOUBLE JEOPARDY!

7-LETTER WORDS

THE ONE THROWN BY MEN IN TRACK & FIELD IS METAL-TIPPED & OVER 8 FEET IN LENGTH	**$200**	WHAT IS
ALTHOUGH FROM FRENCH FOR "MORN-ING", IT NOW REFERS TO A PERFORMANCE IN THE AFTERNOON	**$400**	WHAT IS
THIS FRONT SIDE OF A COIN FEATURES THE PORTRAIT; JEFFERSON ON A NICKEL, FOR EXAMPLE	**$600**	WHAT IS
FROM THE GREEK FOR "STAFF", IT'S A ROD HELD BY A SOVEREIGN AS AN EMBLEM OF POWER OR AUTHORITY	**$800**	WHAT IS
IT'S A MEMBER OF AN ETHNIC GROUP NATIVE TO THE PHILIPPINES, OR THE LANGUAGE ON WHICH PILIPINO IS BASED	**$1000**	WHAT IS

45

DOUBLE JEOPARDY!

7-LETTER WORDS

$200 WHAT IS THE JAVELIN? $200

$400 WHAT IS A MATINEE? $400

$600 WHAT IS THE OBVERSE? $600

$800 WHAT IS A SCEPTER? $800

$1000 WHAT IS TAGALOG? $1000

DOUBLE JEOPARDY!

STATE FLOWERS

Clue	Value	Response
THIS STATE FLOWER OF MASSACHUSETTS SHARES ITS NAME WITH THE SHIP THAT BROUGHT THE PILGRIMS TO THE NEW WORLD	**$200**	WHAT IS
ITS STATE FLOWER IS THE ROCKY MOUNTAIN COLUMBINE	**$400**	WHAT IS
INTERESTINGLY, THIS FRUIT'S BLOSSOM IS THE STATE FLOWER OF DELAWARE, BUT NOT OF GEORGIA	**$600**	WHAT IS
THIS DESERT SHRUB IS SO ABUNDANT IN NEVADA THAT IT GAVE THAT STATE ONE OF ITS NICKNAMES	**$800**	WHAT IS
THE FRAGRANT LIGHT PURPLE VARIETY OF THIS SHRUB IS NEW HAMP-SHIRE'S STATE FLOWER	**$1000**	WHAT IS

DOUBLE JEOPARDY!

STATE FLOWERS

$200 — WHAT IS THE MAYFLOWER? — $200

$400 — WHAT IS COLORADO? — $400

$600 — WHAT IS THE PEACH? — $600

$800 — WHAT IS THE SAGEBRUSH? — $800

$1000 — WHAT IS THE LILAC? — $1000

DOUBLE JEOPARDY!

GRANTS

Clue	Value	Response
THIS FUTURE PRESIDENT WAS WORKING AT HIS FATHER'S LEATHER STORE WHEN THE CIVIL WAR STARTED	$200	WHO IS
IN "SHE DONE HIM WRONG", MAE WEST PROPOSITIONED THIS ACTOR WITH "WHY DON'T YOU COME UP SOMETIME—SEE ME?"	$400	WHO IS
THIS SINGER PUBLISHED A BOOK OF HER OWN "HEART-TO-HEART BIBLE STORIES" FOR CHILDREN	$600	WHO IS
THIS TV PRODUCER WAS MARRIED TO MARY TYLER MOORE UNTIL 1981	$800	WHO IS
THIS 6'8" BASKETBALL FORWARD IS THE SON OF A FORMER DALLAS COWBOYS RUNNING BACK	$1000	WHO IS

49

DOUBLE JEOPARDY!

GRANTS

$200	WHO IS ULYSSES S. GRANT? **$200**
$400	WHO IS CARY GRANT? **$400**
$600	WHO IS AMY GRANT? **$600**
$800	WHO IS GRANT TINKER? **$800**
$1000	WHO IS GRANT HILL? **$1000**

FINAL JEOPARDY!

ENTERTAINERS

IN 1997 THIS ENTERTAINER BECAME THE FIRST AMERICAN NAMED AN HONORARY U.S. VETERAN BY CONGRESS

WHO IS

FINAL JEOPARDY!

ENTERTAINERS

WHO IS BOB HOPE?

JEOPARDY!™

PARTY TIME!

HELOISE SUGGESTS PUTTING FORTUNES INSIDE THESE INFLATABLE ITEMS INSTEAD OF IN COOKIES; THEN LET GUESTS POP THEM	**$100**	WHAT ARE
SIR JOHN SOANE HAD A 3-DAY PARTY AFTER BUYING SETI I's SARCOPHAGUS FOR HIS HOME IN THIS WORLD CAPITAL	**$200**	WHAT IS
A SYNONYM FOR SLUMBER PARTY, IT'S ALSO THE TITLE OF A 1964 ANNETTE FUNICELLO FILM	**$300**	WHAT IS
ON A PARTY INVITATION, THE LETTERS RSVP STAND FOR THE FRENCH PHRASE "REPONDEZ", THIS	**$400**	WHAT IS
A NOISY MOCK SERENADE GIVEN FOR NEWLYWEDS, ITS NAME IS AN ALTERATION OF THE FRENCH WORD CHARIVARI	**$500**	WHAT IS

JEOPARDY!

PARTY TIME!

$100	WHAT ARE BALLOONS?	**$100**
$200	WHAT IS LONDON?	**$200**
$300	WHAT IS "PAJAMA PARTY"?	**$300**
$400	WHAT IS S'IL VOUS PLAIT?	**$400**
$500	WHAT IS A SHIVAREE?	**$500**

54

JEOPARDY!

AMERICAN LITERATURE

Clue	Value	Response
URGED TO MAKE HIS PEACE WITH GOD, THIS "WALDEN" AUTHOR REPLIED "I DID NOT KNOW WE HAD EVER QUARRELED"	$100	WHO IS
CLEMENT C. MOORE'S POEM "A VISIT FROM ST. NICHOLAS" IS MORE POPULARLY KNOWN BY THIS TITLE	$200	WHAT IS
NOVELS BY THIS NATIVE NEWARKER INCLUDE "PORTNOY'S COMPLAINT" & "THE HUMAN STAIN"	$300	WHO IS
IN FRED GIPSON'S NOVEL, THIS "COLORFUL" DOG WITH ONE EAR MISSING ADOPTS A TEXAS FRONTIER FAMILY IN THE 1860s	$400	WHO IS
ONE OF HIS BEST KNOWN WORKS WAS "THE MAN WITHOUT A COUNTRY", BUT HE HIMSELF WAS A MAN FROM BOSTON	$500	WHO IS

JEOPARDY!

AMERICAN LITERATURE

$100	WHO IS HENRY DAVID THOREAU?	**$100**
$200	WHAT IS "('TWAS) THE NIGHT BEFORE CHRISTMAS"?	**$200**
$300	WHO IS PHILIP ROTH?	**$300**
$400	WHO IS OLD YELLER?	**$400**
$500	WHO IS EDWARD EVERETT HALE?	**$500**

JEOPARDY!

"SEA" YA

THE FIRST DAUGHTER BEGINNING IN 1993	**$100**	WHO IS
THIS COMPANY'S V.O. WHISKEY HAD A GOLD & BLACK RIBBON SIGNIFYING THE HORSE RACING COLORS OF ITS FOUNDER	**$200**	WHAT IS
THIS CITY'S ANNUAL SEAFAIR FEATURES VARIOUS WATER SPORTS & A HYDROPLANE RACE ON LAKE WASHINGTON	**$300**	WHAT IS
THIS FISH OF THE GENUS HIPPOCAMPUS HAS THE ABILITY TO CHANGE ITS COLOR TO CONFORM TO ITS BACKGROUND	**$400**	WHAT IS
IN THIS BOBBY DARIN TUNE, "MY LOVER STANDS ON GOLDEN SANDS AND WATCHES THE SHIPS THAT GO SAILING"	**$500**	WHAT IS

JEOPARDY!

"SEA" YA

$100	WHO IS CHELSEA (CLINTON)?	**$100**
$200	WHAT IS THE SEAGRAM COMPANY?	**$200**
$300	WHAT IS SEATTLE?	**$300**
$400	WHAT IS THE SEA HORSE?	**$400**
$500	WHAT IS "BEYOND THE SEA"?	**$500**

JEOPARDY!

ANATOMY

THE INNER PART OF THIS HAS THE BASILAR MEMBRANE; THE OUTER PART HAS THE LOBE	**$100**	WHAT IS
FROM THE GREEK FOR "BREASTBONE", IT'S, WELL . . . THE BREASTBONE	**$200**	WHAT IS
ALSO CALLED THE PATELLA, IT'S HELD IN PLACE BY A LIGAMENT THAT'S AN EXTENSION OF THE TENDON OF THE THIGH MUSCLE	**$300**	WHAT IS
THIS ORGAN SECRETES GLUCAGON AS WELL AS INSULIN	**$400**	WHAT IS
CINDY CRAWFORD'S MOLE, OR ANYBODY'S, IS A COLLECTION OF CELLS WITH A HIGH CONCENTRATION OF THIS PIGMENT	**$500**	WHAT IS

JEOPARDY!

ANATOMY

$100	WHAT IS THE EAR?	$100
$200	WHAT IS THE STERNUM?	$200
$300	WHAT IS THE KNEECAP?	$300
$400	WHAT IS THE PANCREAS?	$400
$500	WHAT IS MELANIN?	$500

JEOPARDY!

TV NOSTALGIA

HE NOT ONLY STARRED ON "CHARLES IN CHARGE", HE WAS OFTEN IN CHARGE AS THE SHOW'S DIRECTOR	**$100**	WHO IS
APPROPRIATE NAME OF THE ANIMATED GIRL ON "PEE-WEE'S PLAYHOUSE" WHO HAD COPPER COINS FOR EYES	**$200**	WHAT IS
IAN FLEMING CAME UP WITH THE NAME NAPOLEON SOLO, ROBERT VAUGHN'S CHARACTER ON THIS SERIES	**$300**	WHAT IS
ONE OF TALLULAH BANKHEAD'S LAST ROLES WAS AS THIS "BATMAN" VILLAINESS NAMED FOR A SPIDER	**$400**	WHO IS
DWAYNE HICKMAN'S BROTHER DARRYL SOMETIMES APPEARED AS THIS CHARACTER'S BROTHER DAVEY	**$500**	WHO IS

61

JEOPARDY!

TV NOSTALGIA

$100	WHO IS SCOTT BAIO?	$100
$200	WHAT IS PENNY?	$200
$300	WHAT IS "THE MAN FROM U.N.C.L.E."?	$300
$400	WHO IS THE BLACK WIDOW?	$400
$500	WHO IS DOBIE GILLIS?	$500

JEOPARDY!

WHO THOUGHT OF THAT?

THIS COUNTRY IS THOUGHT TO HAVE INVENTED GUN-POWDER, AS WELL AS SOY SAUCE	**$100**	WHAT IS
CLEMENT ADER CREATED THIS TYPE OF SOUND SYSTEM THAT USED 2 MIKES FEEDING SEPARATE HEADPHONES	**$200**	WHAT IS
THE GERMAN HEINKEL He-280 OF 1941 WAS THE FIRST JET FIGHTER TO HAVE ONE OF THESE IN CASE OF EMERGENCY	**$300**	WHAT IS
HE FIRST DETERMINED THAT ENERGY EQUALS MASS TIMES THE VELOCITY OF LIGHT SQUARED	**$400**	WHO IS
IN 1965 STEPHANIE KWOLEK DEVELOPED THIS MATERIAL USED IN BULLETPROOF VESTS	**$500**	WHAT IS

JEOPARDY!

WHO THOUGHT OF THAT?

$100 — WHAT IS CHINA? — $100

$200 — WHAT IS STEREO? — $200

$300 — WHAT IS AN EJECTION SEAT? — $300

$400 — WHO IS ALBERT EINSTEIN? — $400

$500 — WHAT IS KEVLAR? — $500

DOUBLE JEOPARDY!

REDS

HIS VARIETY SHOW RAN FOR 20 YEARS, 17 ON CBS	**$200**	WHO IS
BORN AARON CHWATT, HE WON AN OSCAR FOR "SAYONARA" UNDER THIS NAME	**$400**	WHO IS
HE DIED OCTOBER 11, 1991 AFTER COLLAPSING AT A REHEARSAL OF HIS NEW TV SERIES, "THE ROYAL FAMILY"	**$600**	WHO IS
FROM 1934 TO 1939 HE WAS THE VOICE OF THE CINCINNATI REDS	**$800**	WHO IS
IN 1995 LENNY WILKENS BROKE THIS MAN'S RECORD AS THE NBA's WINNINGEST COACH	**$1000**	WHO IS

DOUBLE JEOPARDY!

REDS

$200   WHO IS
RED SKELTON?   **$200**

$400   WHO IS
RED BUTTONS?   **$400**

$600   WHO IS
REDD FOXX?   **$600**

$800   WHO IS
RED BARBER?   **$800**

$1000   WHO IS
RED AUERBACH?   **$1000**

DOUBLE JEOPARDY!

HISTORIC NAMES

HIS EPITAPH READS, "FOUNDER OF BOYS TOWN AND LOVER OF CHRIST AND MAN"	**$200**	WHO IS
WHILE ROUNDING THE TIP OF SOUTH AMERICA IN 1520, THIS PORTUGUESE EXPLORER NAMED CAPE VIRGINES & PATAGONIA	**$400**	WHO IS
IT'S BEEN SAID THAT THE 1831 RUSSIAN CAPTURE OF WARSAW INSPIRED HIM TO WRITE HIS C MINOR ETUDE	**$600**	WHO IS
THIS FAMILY THAT ONCE CONTROLLED NICARAGUA SAW 2 MEMBERS KILLED—THE FATHER IN 1956, A SON IN 1980	**$800**	WHO ARE
THIS DISCOVERER OF URANUS THOUGHT THE SUN WAS AN INHABITED BODY WITH A LUMINOUS ATMOSPHERE	**$1000**	WHO IS

DOUBLE JEOPARDY!

HISTORIC NAMES

$200	WHO IS FATHER EDWARD FLANAGAN?	**$200**
$400	WHO IS FERDINAND MAGELLAN?	**$400**
$600	WHO IS FREDERIC CHOPIN?	**$600**
$800	WHO ARE THE SOMOZAS?	**$800**
$1000	WHO IS WILLIAM HERSCHEL?	**$1000**

DOUBLE JEOPARDY!

AUSTEN-TATIOUS

Clue	Value	Response
JANE AUSTEN SAID ELIZABETH BENNET, THE HEROINE OF THIS NOVEL, WAS "AS DELIGHTFUL A CREATURE AS EVER APPEARED IN PRINT"	$200	WHAT IS
AFTER HER UNSUC-CESSFUL & MEDDLE-SOME MATCHMAKING, THIS TITLE CHARACTER REALIZES SHE LOVES MR. KNIGHTLEY	$400	WHO IS
THIS AUTHOR OF "OR-LANDO" SAID "OF ALL THE GREAT WRITERS" JANE "IS THE MOST DIFFICULT TO CATCH IN THE ACT OF GREATNESS"	$600	WHO IS
WHILE PRINCE REGENT DURING HIS FATHER'S MADNESS, THIS KING HAD A SET OF AUSTEN'S NOVELS IN EACH OF HIS RESIDENCES	$800	WHO IS
THIS TITLE ABBEY IS THE HOME OF CLERGYMAN HENRY TILNEY	$1000	WHAT IS

DOUBLE JEOPARDY!

AUSTEN-TATIOUS

$200	WHAT IS "PRIDE AND PREJUDICE"?	**$200**
$400	WHO IS EMMA (WOODHOUSE)?	**$400**
$600	WHO IS VIRGINIA WOOLF?	**$600**
$800	WHO IS GEORGE IV?	**$800**
$1000	WHAT IS NORTHANGER ABBEY?	**$1000**

DOUBLE JEOPARDY!

IT'S A GROUP THING

ROBBY KRIEGER, RAY MANZAREK, JOHN DENSMORE & JIM MORRISON	**$200**	WHAT IS
DALTON TRUMBO, RING LARNDER, JR. & 8 OTHER SHOWBIZ NOTABLES	**$400**	WHAT ARE
AYKROYD, BELUSHI, CURTIN, MORRIS, CHASE, RADNER & NEWMAN WERE THESE "PLAYERS"	**$600**	WHAT ARE
TASTY QUARTET CONSISTING OF BINGO, DROOPER, FLEEGLE & SNORKY	**$800**	WHAT IS
TO THE ANCIENT GREEKS, THEY WERE LACHESIS, CLOTHO & ATROPOS	**$1000**	WHAT ARE

DOUBLE JEOPARDY!

IT'S A GROUP THING

$200   WHAT IS THE DOORS? $200

$400   WHAT ARE THE HOLLYWOOD TEN? $400

$600   WHAT ARE THE NOT READY FOR PRIME TIME PLAYERS? $600

$800   WHAT IS THE BANANA SPLITS? $800

$1000   WHAT ARE THE FATES? $1000

DOUBLE JEOPARDY!

PARISIANS

WHEN LENIN MOVED TO PARIS IN 1908, HE NATURALLY SETTLED ON THIS BANK OF THE SEINE	**$200**	WHAT IS
FOR SPEAKING TOO "CANDIDE"LY, HE DID TIME IN THE BASTILLE, BUT LATER LIVED IN A MANSION ON ILE ST-LOUIS	**$400**	WHO IS
THE VOICE OF THIS WOMAN, BORN IN PARIS IN 1915, EVOKES THE CITY IN SONGS LIKE "NON, JE NE REGRETTE RIEN"	**$600**	WHO IS
IN THE 1880s HE INTRODUCED HIS BROTHER & ROOMMATE, VINCENT, TO THE IMPRESSIONISTS	**$800**	WHO IS
THIS SAINT TAUGHT AT THE UNIVERSITY OF PARIS WHILE WORKING ON "SUMMA THEOLOGICA" IN THE 13th CENTURY	**$1000**	WHO IS

DOUBLE JEOPARDY!

PARISIANS

$200	WHAT IS THE LEFT BANK?	$200
$400	WHO IS VOLTAIRE?	$400
$600	WHO IS EDITH PIAF?	$600
$800	WHO IS THEO VAN GOGH?	$800
$1000	WHO IS THOMAS AQUINAS?	$1000

DOUBLE JEOPARDY!

QUESTIONS, QUESTIONS

SEPT. 20, 1999 WAS THE 15th ANNIVERSARY OF THE PREMIERE OF THIS TV SHOW WITH TONY DANZA AS A DOMESTIC	**$200**	WHAT IS
THIS TITLE MUSICAL QUESTION ASKED BY ELVIS PRESLEY & DONNY OSMOND HAS BEEN AROUND SINCE THE '20s	**$400**	WHAT IS
COPS ASK THIS OF SOMEONE IN A HURRY; IN 1871 A GOOD ANSWER WOULD HAVE BEEN "CHICAGO"	**$600**	WHAT IS
FREUD CALLED IT THE GREAT QUESTION HE COULDN'T ANSWER "DESPITE 30 YEARS OF RESEARCH INTO THE FEMININE SOUL"	**$800**	WHAT IS
IT'S THE LATIN PHRASE OF ST. PETER'S TRADITIONAL QUESTION TO JESUS, "WHITHER GOEST THOU?"	**$1000**	WHAT IS

DOUBLE JEOPARDY!
QUESTIONS, QUESTIONS

$200 — (WHAT IS) "WHO'S THE BOSS?" — $200

$400 — (WHAT IS) "ARE YOU LONESOME TONIGHT?" — $400

$600 — (WHAT IS) "WHERE'S THE FIRE?" — $600

$800 — (WHAT IS) "WHAT DOES A WOMAN (REALLY) WANT?" — $800

$1000 — (WHAT IS) "QUO VADIS?" — $1000

FINAL JEOPARDY!
IN THE KITCHEN

NOW IN OVER 40 MILLION
U.S. KITCHENS, THIS TYPE
OF PRODUCT WAS ILLEGAL
IN NYC UNTIL 1997

WHAT ARE

FINAL JEOPARDY!

IN THE KITCHEN

WHAT ARE
GARBAGE DISPOSALS?

JEOPARDY!™

A DRIVING TOUR

DRIVE BY THE COPS WHEN YOU PUT THE PEDAL TO THE METAL ON MOST OF THESE HIGH-SPEED GERMAN HIGHWAYS	$100	WHAT ARE
KRASNAYA PLOSHCHAD IS THE LOCAL NAME FOR THIS SQUARE YOU CAN DRIVE BY, BUT NOT ACROSS	$200	WHAT IS
HIGH DEGREE FREE-MASONS KNOW IT CAN BE HARD TO DRIVE BY THIS L.A. AUDITORIUM ON JEFFERSON BLVD. ON OSCAR NIGHT	$300	WHAT IS
YOU'LL REACH THE PRESIDENT'S OFFICE IN THIS COUNTRY DRIVING TO THE UNION BUILD-INGS ON GOVERNMENT AVE. IN PRETORIA	$400	WHAT IS
DRIVE DOWN OBALA VOJVODE STEPE IN THIS CITY & RELIVE THE STREET'S MOST FAMOUS MOMENT OF JUNE 28, 1914	$500	WHAT IS

JEOPARDY!

A DRIVING TOUR

$100	WHAT ARE AUTOBAHNS?	**$100**
$200	WHAT IS RED SQUARE?	**$200**
$300	WHAT IS THE SHRINE AUDITORIUM?	**$300**
$400	WHAT IS SOUTH AFRICA?	**$400**
$500	WHAT IS SARAJEVO?	**$500**

JEOPARDY!

THE QUOTABLE JOHN ADAMS

IN 1793 JOHN ADAMS SAID OF IT, "MY COUNTRY HAS IN ITS WISDOM CONTRIVED FOR ME THE MOST INSIGNIFICANT OFFICE"	**$100**	WHAT IS
"YOU AND I OUGHT NOT TO DIE BEFORE WE HAVE EXPLAINED OURSELVES TO EACH OTHER", ADAMS WROTE HIM YEARS BEFORE JULY 4, 1826	**$200**	WHO IS
IN 1779 ADAMS WROTE TO HER, "I MUST NOT WRITE A WORD TO YOU ABOUT POLITICS, BECAUSE YOU ARE A WOMAN"	**$300**	WHO IS
"FACTS ARE STUBBORN THINGS", ADAMS SAID IN DEFENSE OF BRITISH SOLDIERS INVOLVED IN THIS 1770 CLASH	**$400**	WHAT IS
ADAMS WISHED FOR ONE "OF LAWS, AND NOT OF MEN", BUT FELT THAT "FEAR IS THE FOUNDATION OF MOST"	**$500**	WHAT IS

JEOPARDY!

THE QUOTABLE JOHN ADAMS

$100 · WHAT IS THE VICE PRESIDENCY? · $100

$200 · WHO IS THOMAS JEFFERSON? · $200

$300 · WHO IS ABIGAIL ADAMS? · $300

$400 · WHAT IS THE BOSTON MASSACRE? · $400

$500 · WHAT IS GOVERNMENT? · $500

JEOPARDY!

ACTORS & ACTRESSES

Clue	Value	Response
HER REAL NAME IS DONNA MILLER; ANOTHER ACTRESS HAD THE SAME NAME, SO SHE CHANGED HERS TO THIS	$100	WHAT IS
IN THE 1930s THIS HEARTTHROB WAS SO POPULAR HE WAS KNOWN AS "THE KING OF HOLLYWOOD"	$200	WHO IS
OF JOHN GIELGUD, HENRY IRVING OR LAURENCE OLIVIER, THE FIRST ENGLISH ACTOR TO BE KNIGHTED	$300	WHO IS
THIS "FAIR LADY" OF FILM STARRED ON BROADWAY IN A NON-MUSICAL VERSION OF "GIGI" IN 1951	$400	WHO IS
HE ONCE PLAYED YOUNG TOM HUGHES ON "AS THE WORLD TURNS" BUT HE'S BETTER KNOWN AS JOHN-BOY WALTON	$500	WHO IS

JEOPARDY!

ACTORS & ACTRESSES

$100	WHAT IS DONNA MILLS?	$100
$200	WHO IS CLARK GABLE?	$200
$300	WHO IS (SIR) HENRY IRVING?	$300
$400	WHO IS AUDREY HEPBURN?	$400
$500	WHO IS RICHARD THOMAS?	$500

JEOPARDY!

EASY AS "PIE"

Clue	Value	Response
LITTLE JACK HORNER STUCK HIS THUMB IN THIS & PULLED OUT A PLUM	$100	WHAT IS
THIS NO. 1 HIT BY DON McLEAN MOURNED THE DEATH OF BUDDY HOLLY	$200	WHAT IS
THIS PHRASE REFERS TO THE DECEPTIVELY ROSY PROSPECT OF FUTURE EVENTS	$300	WHAT IS
IT'S A REPRESENTATION OF FACTS PRESENTED AS A CIRCLE DIVIDED INTO SECTORS OF RELATIVE SIZES	$400	WHAT IS
CREATED BY PAUL TERRY, THE FAST-TALKING HECKLE & JECKLE ARE 2 OF THESE CROW RELATIVES	$500	WHAT ARE

JEOPARDY!

EASY AS "PIE"

$100	WHAT IS HIS CHRISTMAS PIE?	**$100**
$200	WHAT IS "AMERICAN PIE"?	**$200**
$300	WHAT IS PIE IN THE SKY?	**$300**
$400	WHAT IS A PIE CHART (OR GRAPH)?	**$400**
$500	WHAT ARE MAGPIES?	**$500**

JEOPARDY!

PUNISHMENT

GET YOUR COME-UPPANCE & YOU GET YOUR "JUST" THESE, NOT ICE CREAM & CAKE	**$100**	WHAT ARE
IN PRISON SLANG, "THE HOLE" IS THIS TYPE OF CONFINEMENT	**$200**	WHAT IS
A CAUSTIC VERBAL ATTACK WHEN DONE WITH A TONGUE, OR A MORE PAINFUL ONE DONE WITH A WHIP	**$300**	WHAT IS
A VERB MEANING TO GIVE PERMISSION, OR A PENALTY, ECONOMIC OR OTHERWISE	**$400**	WHAT IS
LITERALLY, IT MEANS DRAWING A PERSON UNDER A SHIP FROM SIDE TO SIDE OR FROM BOW TO STERN	**$500**	WHAT IS

JEOPARDY!

PUNISHMENT

$100	WHAT ARE DESERTS?	**$100**
$200	WHAT IS SOLITARY CONFINEMENT?	**$200**
$300	WHAT IS A LASHING?	**$300**
$400	WHAT IS SANCTION?	**$400**
$500	WHAT IS KEELHAULING?	**$500**

JEOPARDY!

1941

TIME MAGAZINE NAMED THIS ANIMATED BABY ELEPHANT ITS "MAMMAL OF THE YEAR"	**$100**	WHO IS
IN JULY HE WAS MADE LIEUTENANT GENERAL & NAMED COMMANDER IN CHIEF OF ALL U.S. FORCES IN THE FAR EAST	**$200**	WHO IS
TITLE TRAIN IN A 1941 GLENN MILLER HIT	**$300**	WHAT IS
IN 1941 GEORGE HALAS COACHED THIS TEAM TO A 37-9 VICTORY OVER THE NEW YORK GIANTS IN THE NFL TITLE GAME	**$400**	WHAT ARE
IN MAY 1941 HE & HIS COMRADES ORGANIZED THE LEAGUE FOR THE INDEPENDENCE OF VIETNAM	**$500**	WHO IS

JEOPARDY!

1941

$100	WHO IS DUMBO?	$100
$200	WHO IS GENERAL DOUGLAS MacARTHUR?	$200
$300	WHAT IS THE "CHATTANOOGA CHOO CHOO"?	$300
$400	WHAT ARE THE CHICAGO BEARS?	$400
$500	WHO IS HO CHI MINH?	$500

90

DOUBLE JEOPARDY!

WORD & PHRASE ORIGINS

Clue	Value	Response
THE FRENCH FOR "SCANDAL" GAVE US THE NAME OF THIS HIGH-KICKING DANCE POPULAR IN MUSIC HALLS OF THE 19th CENTURY	$200	WHAT IS
THIS PHRASE FOR TAKING A BREAK FROM A LONG PERIOD OF SITTING GOES BACK TO 19th CENTURY BASEBALL	$400	WHAT IS
AN ILLUSTRATED "GIRL" & A VARIATION ON THE MARTINI ARE NAMED FOR THIS U.S. ARTIST	$600	WHO IS
FROM THE ITALIAN FOR "CHATTER", IT'S A PERSON WHO CLAIMS KNOWLEDGE OR SKILL HE DOESN'T HAVE	$800	WHAT IS
2 GREEK WORDS FOR "LONG LIFE" GIVE US THIS WORD WHICH REFERS TO A DIET OR LIFESTYLE SAID TO PROLONG LIFE	$1000	WHAT IS

DOUBLE JEOPARDY!
WORD & PHRASE ORIGINS

$200	WHAT IS THE CANCAN?	**$200**
$400	WHAT IS THE SEVENTH-INNING STRETCH?	**$400**
$600	WHO IS CHARLES DANA GIBSON?	**$600**
$800	WHAT IS A CHARLATAN?	**$800**
$1000	WHAT IS MACROBIOTIC?	**$1000**

DOUBLE JEOPARDY!

ASTRONOMY

Clue	Value	Response
ON FEBRUARY 11, 1999 IT AGAIN BECAME THE FARTHEST PLANET FROM THE SUN & WILL REMAIN SO FOR 248 YEARS	$200	WHAT IS
ALNILAM, ALNITAK & MINTAKA ARE THE 3 STARS OF THIS CONSTELLATION'S BELT	$400	WHAT IS
AMONG THESE OBJECTS, ENCKE'S HAS AN ORBITAL PERIOD OF 3.3 YEARS; TAGO-SATO-KOSAKA, 420,000 YEARS	$600	WHAT ARE
IN 1937 IN WHEATON, ILLINOIS, GROTE REBER BUILT THE FIRST ONE OF THESE TELESCOPES USING A PARABOLIC DISH	$800	WHAT IS
THIS ALEXANDRIAN ASTRONOMER DISCUSSES ECLIPSES IN BOOK VI OF HIS 2nd CENTURY WORK "ALMAGEST"	$1000	WHO IS

DOUBLE JEOPARDY!

ASTRONOMY

$200	WHAT IS PLUTO?	**$200**
$400	WHAT IS ORION?	**$400**
$600	WHAT ARE COMETS?	**$600**
$800	WHAT IS A RADIO TELESCOPE?	**$800**
$1000	WHO IS PTOLEMY?	**$1000**

DOUBLE JEOPARDY!

COOKING

WHEN A PIE HAS 2 OF THESE, THE TOP ONE MAY BE "WOVEN" IN A LATTICE DESIGN	**$200**	WHAT ARE
DON'T THROW AWAY THIS PART OF A WATERMELON; MANY COOKS PICKLE IT	**$400**	WHAT IS
POPULAR IN ASIA, THIS COOKING UTENSIL THAT USUALLY HAS 2 HANDLES IS PERFECT FOR STIR-FRYING	**$600**	WHAT IS
MIX DRIED, POUNDED MEAT WITH FAT & BERRIES TO MAKE THIS TRADITIONAL FOOD OF NATIVE AMERICANS	**$800**	WHAT IS
THIS TERM FOR A TYPE OF INDIAN COOKING COMES FROM THE NAME OF THE HOT OVEN IT USES	**$1000**	WHAT IS

95

DOUBLE JEOPARDY!

COOKING

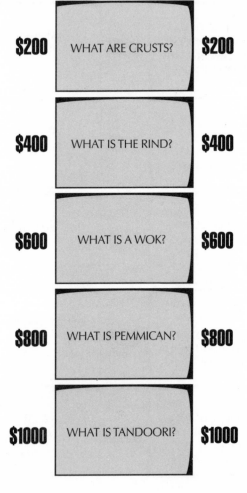

$200	WHAT ARE CRUSTS?	$200
$400	WHAT IS THE RIND?	$400
$600	WHAT IS A WOK?	$600
$800	WHAT IS PEMMICAN?	$800
$1000	WHAT IS TANDOORI?	$1000

DOUBLE JEOPARDY!

ALASKA

Clue	Value	Response
THIS 2,000-MILE RIVER WAS THE PRINCIPAL TRANSPORTATION ROUTE DURING THE EARLY MINING DAYS OF ALASKA	$200	WHAT IS
IN 1942 THIS NATION'S FORCES OCCUPIED ATTU & KISKA IN THE ALEUTIAN ISLANDS	$400	WHAT IS
NUMBER OF CONGRESSMEN REPRESENTING ALASKA IN THE U.S. HOUSE	$600	WHAT IS
AT ONLY 2½ MILES AWAY, LITTLE DIOMEDE ISLAND IN THIS STRAIT IS THE CLOSEST PART OF NORTH AMERICA TO ASIA	$800	WHAT IS
THIS SECRETARY OF STATE BOUGHT ALASKA FROM RUSSIA IN 1867 AT ABOUT 2 CENTS AN ACRE, A BARGAIN PRICE	$1000	WHO IS

DOUBLE JEOPARDY!

ALASKA

$200	WHAT IS THE YUKON RIVER?	**$200**
$400	WHAT IS JAPAN?	**$400**
$600	WHAT IS 1?	**$600**
$800	WHAT IS THE BERING STRAIT?	**$800**
$1000	WHO IS WILLIAM SEWARD?	**$1000**

DOUBLE JEOPARDY!

ARCHITECTURE

Clue	Value	Response
LUIGI MORETTI DESIGNED BUILDINGS FOR MUSSOLINI & THIS WASHINGTON, D.C. COMPLEX THAT LED TO NIXON'S FALL	**$200**	WHAT IS
THIS STYLE INFLUENCED BY THE ROMANS IS NAMED FOR ENGLAND'S 4 KINGS BETWEEN 1714 & 1830	**$400**	WHAT IS
524 FIRMS COMPETED TO DESIGN A NEW LIBRARY AT THIS CITY TO RECALL THE ANCIENT ONE	**$600**	WHAT IS
HABITAT, BUILT FOR THIS CITY'S EXPO 67, WAS A REVOLUTIONARY PREFABRICATED HOUSING COMPLEX	**$800**	WHAT IS
THIS ARCHITECTURALLY CONTROVERSIAL CENTER NAMED FOR A FRENCH PRESIDENT OPENED IN 1977	**$1000**	WHAT IS

DOUBLE JEOPARDY!

ARCHITECTURE

$200	WHAT IS WATERGATE?	**$200**
$400	WHAT IS GEORGIAN?	**$400**
$600	WHAT IS ALEXANDRIA?	**$600**
$800	WHAT IS MONTREAL?	**$800**
$1000	WHAT IS THE POMPIDOU CENTER?	**$1000**

DOUBLE JEOPARDY!

BIG SCREEN BADDIES

DANIEL STERN & JOE PESCI PLAYED THE BURGLARS WHO TORMENTED THIS YOUNG ACTOR WHEN HE WAS "HOME ALONE"	**$200**	WHO IS
COL. TAVINGTON IS A REPTILIAN BRITISH OFFICER IN THIS MEL GIBSON REVOLU-TIONARY WAR FILM	**$400**	WHAT IS
IN 1978 GENE HACKMAN PLANNED TO DESTROY THE WEST COAST OF THE U.S. AS THIS SUPERHERO-FIGHTING VILLIAN	**$600**	WHO IS
A PERENNIAL GOOD GUY NOW, IN BRUCE LEE'S "RETURN OF THE DRAGON" THIS AMERI-CAN TV STAR PLAYED A MARTIAL ARTS VILLIAN	**$800**	WHO IS
HE'S THE MYSTERIOUS CRIME LORD WHO TERRIFIES FELLOW CROOKS IN "THE USUAL SUSPECTS"	**$1000**	WHO IS

DOUBLE JEOPARDY!

BIG SCREEN BADDIES

$200	WHO IS MACAULAY CULKIN?
$400	WHAT IS "THE PATRIOT"?
$600	WHO IS LEX LUTHOR?
$800	WHO IS CHUCK NORRIS?
$1000	WHO IS KEYSER SOZE?

CHILDREN'S BOOKS & AUTHORS

HE ALSO CREATED
A 2-LETTER LAND
CALLED IX

WHO IS

FINAL JEOPARDY!

CHILDREN'S BOOKS & AUTHORS

WHO IS L. FRANK BAUM?

JEOPARDY!

JOB BANK

"SUPER", WHEN REFERRING TO A PERSON WHO TAKES CARE OF AN APARTMENT HOUSE, IS SHORT FOR THIS	**$100**	WHAT IS
ONE OF THE JOBS OF A DESHI IN JAPAN IS TO WASH THE PLACES ON THESE ATHLETES THAT THEY CAN'T REACH THEMSELVES	**$200**	WHAT ARE
PRECEDING "LEADER" IT MAKES YOU HEAD OF A GANG OF THUGS; BEFORE "MASTER", HEAD OF A GANG OF CIRCUS ACTS	**$300**	WHAT IS
IN ENGLAND A DRUGGIST IS CALLED THIS, WHICH TO US SOUNDS LIKE A SCIENTIST	**$400**	WHAT IS
ELIZABETH II DOESN'T DO THIS HERSELF; SHE HAS A HEREDITARY GRAND ALMONER TO DO IT FOR HER	**$500**	WHAT IS

JEOPARDY!

JOB BANK

$100 WHAT IS SUPERINTENDENT? **$100**

$200 WHAT ARE SUMO WRESTLERS? **$200**

$300 WHAT IS RING? **$300**

$400 WHAT IS A CHEMIST? **$400**

$500 WHAT IS GIVE OUT CHARITY? **$500**

JEOPARDY!

APRIL

Clue	Value	Response
THE CHRISTIAN CELEBRATION OF EASTER & THIS JEWISH FESTIVAL ALSO KNOWN AS PESACH CAN BOTH OCCUR IN APRIL	$100	WHAT IS
HE ABDICATED FOR THE FIRST TIME IN APRIL 1814	$200	WHO IS
POCAHONTAS MARRIED THIS MAN ON APRIL 5, 1614	$300	WHO IS
EACH YEAR ENGLISH-SPEAKING CANADIANS HONOR THIS SAINT ON APRIL 23	$400	WHO IS
IN 46 B.C. THIS MAN ORDERED THE ADDITION OF A 30th DAY TO APRIL	$500	WHO IS

JEOPARDY!

APRIL

$100 WHAT IS PASSOVER? **$100**

$200 WHO IS NAPOLEON? **$200**

$300 WHO IS JOHN ROLFE? **$300**

$400 WHO IS ST. GEORGE? **$400**

$500 WHO IS JULIUS CAESAR? **$500**

JEOPARDY!

LONG-RUNNING TV SHOWS

THIS PBS CHILDREN'S PROGRAM HAS BEEN SPONSORED BY THE LETTERS OF THE ALPHABET SINCE 1969	**$100**	WHAT IS
OF THE ORIGINAL CAST MEMBERS ON THIS DRAMA, STEVEN HILL AS D.A. ADAM SCHIFF LASTED THE LONGEST	**$200**	WHAT IS
AFTER 35 YEARS, THIS SOAP OPERA'S "SEARCH" ENDED IN 1986	**$300**	WHAT IS
BY THE TIME THIS SITCOM ENDED, FRED MacMURRAY'S CHARACTER HAD BECOME A GRANDFATHER TO TRIPLET BOYS	**$400**	WHAT IS
AS A BOY, TIM RUSSERT, FUTURE HOST OF THIS SHOW, WATCHED IT WITH HIS FATHER	**$500**	WHAT IS

JEOPARDY!

LONG-RUNNING TV SHOWS

$100	WHAT IS "SESAME STREET"?	**$100**
$200	WHAT IS "LAW & ORDER"?	**$200**
$300	WHAT IS "SEARCH FOR TOMORROW"?	**$300**
$400	WHAT IS "MY THREE SONS"?	**$400**
$500	WHAT IS "MEET THE PRESS"?	**$500**

JEOPARDY!

FAIRY TALE FEMMES

ONE OF THE FEW TIMES SHE LAUGHS IN WONDERLAND IS WHEN SHE HAS TO USE A FLAMINGO TO PLAY CROQUET	**$100**	WHO IS
SHE ATE THE WINDOW PANE OF THE WITCH'S COTTAGE	**$200**	WHO IS
SHE WOULD HAVE BEEN POPULAR IN THE '60s; SHE WAS ALWAYS LETTING HER HAIR DOWN	**$300**	WHO IS
THE BROTHERS GRIMM GAVE NO NAME FOR THE MILLER'S DAUGHTER WHO GUESSED THE NAME OF THIS LITTLE MAN	**$400**	WHO IS
HE WROTE A LITTLE ABOUT WOMEN: "THE LITTLE MATCH GIRL", "THE LITTLE MERMAID"...	**$500**	WHO IS

111

JEOPARDY!

FAIRY TALE FEMMES

$100	WHO IS ALICE?	**$100**
$200	WHO IS GRETEL?	**$200**
$300	WHO IS RAPUNZEL?	**$300**
$400	WHO IS RUMPELSTILTSKIN?	**$400**
$500	WHO IS HANS CHRISTIAN ANDERSEN?	**$500**

JEOPARDY!

"HORSE" SENSE

Clue	Value	Response
HE PURSUES ICHABOD CRANE THROUGH SLEEPY HOLLOW	$100	WHO IS
PUNGENT GROUND UP ARMORACIA RUSTICANA ROOTS USED AS A CONDIMENT	$200	WHAT IS
THIS OGLALA SIOUX LEADER DIED IN CAPTIVITY IN SEPTEMBER 1877	$300	WHO IS
A LITTLE-KNOWN, UNEXPECTEDLY SUCCESSFUL POLITICAL CANDIDATE	$400	WHAT IS
UNIT EQUAL TO 33,000 FOOT-POUNDS PER MINUTE	$500	WHAT IS

JEOPARDY!

"HORSE" SENSE

$100	WHO IS THE HEADLESS HORSEMAN?	$100
$200	WHAT IS HORSERADISH?	$200
$300	WHO IS CRAZY HORSE?	$300
$400	WHAT IS A DARK HORSE?	$400
$500	WHAT IS HORSEPOWER?	$500

JEOPARDY!™

AROUND THE WORLD

BOOMTOWN 1910 IS A RECREATED FRONTIER STREET AT A MUSEUM IN SASKATOON IN THIS CANADIAN PROVINCE	**$100**	WHAT IS
THE EFIK PEOPLE OF THIS CONTINENT ARE CLOSELY RELATED TO THE IBIBIO	**$200**	WHAT IS
COSTA RICA'S NAME TRANSLATES TO THIS IN ENGLISH	**$300**	WHAT IS
THIS SCANDINAVIAN COUNTRY IS QUITE FLAT; ITS HIGHEST POINT, YDING SKOVHOJ, IS JUST 568 HIGH	**$400**	WHAT IS
IF YOU'RE A NATIVE MALDIVIAN, YOU HAIL FROM AN ISLAND COUNTRY IN THIS OCEAN	**$500**	WHAT IS

JEOPARDY!

AROUND THE WORLD

$100 WHAT IS SASKATCHEWAN? **$100**

$200 WHAT IS AFRICA? **$200**

$300 WHAT IS RICH COAST? **$300**

$400 WHAT IS DENMARK? **$400**

$500 WHAT IS THE INDIAN OCEAN? **$500**

DOUBLE JEOPARDY!

IT'S ABOUT TIME

0 DEGREES LONGITUDE, THE "PRIME" ONE OF THESE, PASSES THROUGH GREENWICH OBSERVATORY	**$200**	WHAT IS
IN 1752 GREAT BRITAIN IMPOSED THIS CALENDAR ON ALL ITS POSSESSIONS, INCLUDING THE AMERICAN COLONIES	**$400**	WHAT IS
TIMEPIECE MENTIONED IN THE INTRODUCTION TO "DAYS OF OUR LIVES"	**$600**	WHAT IS
THE WORLD IS DIVIDED INTO 23 FULL TIME ZONES & 2 HALF TIME ZONES; THE HALF ZONES ARE SEPARATED BY THIS	**$800**	WHAT IS
TIME IN THE U.S. IS DETERMINED BY THE NATIONAL INSTITUTE OF STANDARDS & TECHNOLOGY WHOSE ATOMIC CLOCK IS IN THIS COLORADO CITY	**$1000**	WHAT IS

DOUBLE JEOPARDY!

IT'S ABOUT TIME

$200	WHAT IS THE PRIME MERIDIAN?	**$200**
$400	WHAT IS THE GREGORIAN CALENDAR?	**$400**
$600	WHAT IS AN HOURGLASS?	**$600**
$800	WHAT IS THE INTERNATIONAL DATE LINE?	**$800**
$1000	WHAT IS BOULDER?	**$1000**

DOUBLE JEOPARDY!

ASIAN CITIES

IN A 1940 FILM SABU WAS "THE THIEF OF" THIS CITY	**$200**	WHAT IS
YOU COULD CALL BENAZIR BHUTTO, BORN IN THIS COUNTRY'S LARGEST CITY, THE KARACHI KID	**$400**	WHAT IS
IT HOSTED THE 1972 WINTER OLYMPICS & LENDS ITS NAME TO ONE OF JAPAN'S OLDEST BRANDS OF BEER	**$600**	WHAT IS
IN THIS CITY YOU CAN VISIT AN UPLIFTING MUSEUM OF KHMER ART, OR TUOL SLENG, A MUSEUM OF TORTURE & MURDER	**$800**	WHAT IS
UH, JUST ONE MORE THING ... IT'S SRI LANKA'S MOST IMPORTANT PORT	**$1000**	WHAT IS

DOUBLE JEOPARDY!

ASIAN CITIES

$200	WHAT IS BAGHDAD?	**$200**
$400	WHAT IS PAKISTAN?	**$400**
$600	WHAT IS SAPPORO?	**$600**
$800	WHAT IS PHNOM PENH?	**$800**
$1000	WHAT IS COLOMBO?	**$1000**

DOUBLE JEOPARDY!

RHYMES WITH RAIN

WHEN WORKING OUT, MANY FOLLOW THE OLD SAYING, "NO PAIN, NO" THIS	**$200**	WHAT IS
AS CARLY SIMON COULD TELL YOU, IT'S A SYNONYM FOR NARCISSISTIC	**$400**	WHAT IS
WORLD BOOK DESCRIBES IT AS A "GRAYISH-PINK, JELLYLIKE BALL WITH MANY RIDGES AND GROOVES"	**$600**	WHAT IS
A COIL OF YARN	**$800**	WHAT IS
IN EARLY SCOTLAND, IT WAS A PERSON OF RANK; MACBETH WAS ONE OF GLAMIS, THEN CAWDOR	**$1000**	WHAT IS

DOUBLE JEOPARDY!

RHYMES WITH RAIN

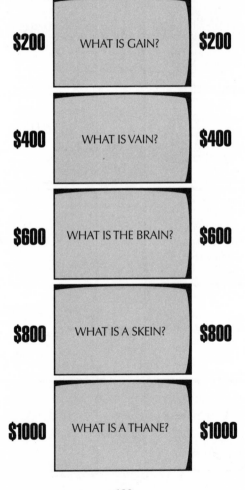

$200   WHAT IS GAIN?   **$200**

$400   WHAT IS VAIN?   **$400**

$600   WHAT IS THE BRAIN?   **$600**

$800   WHAT IS A SKEIN?   **$800**

$1000   WHAT IS A THANE?   **$1000**

DOUBLE JEOPARDY!

THE SOCIAL SCIENCES

Clue	Value	Response
A SPECIALIST IN THE SCIENCE OF LANGUAGE, OR SOMEONE WHO SPEAKS MANY LANGUAGES	**$200**	WHAT IS
FROM 1932 TO 1947 THIS POLLSTER WAS RESEARCH DIRECTOR AT THE YOUNG & RUBICAM AD AGENCY	**$400**	WHO IS
FROM THE GREEK FOR "SOUL", THIS SOCIAL SCIENCE HAS CLINICAL, DEVELOPMENTAL & SOCIAL BRANCHES	**$600**	WHAT IS
THIS –OLOGY DEALS SPECIFICALLY WITH PUNISHMENT & THE MANAGEMENT OF PRISONS	**$800**	WHAT IS
THE DEVELOPMENT STUDIES INSTITUTE IS PART OF THE LONDON SCHOOL OF THIS	**$1000**	WHAT IS

DOUBLE JEOPARDY!

THE SOCIAL SCIENCES

$200	WHAT IS A LINGUIST?	**$200**
$400	WHO IS GEORGE GALLUP?	**$400**
$600	WHAT IS PSYCHOLOGY?	**$600**
$800	WHAT IS PENOLOGY?	**$800**
$1000	WHAT IS ECONOMICS (& POLITICAL SCIENCE)?	**$1000**

DOUBLE JEOPARDY!

ART & ARTISTS

IN OCTOBER 1888 THIS PAINTER JOINED VAN GOGH IN ARLES; HE FLED AFTER THAT UGLY EAR INCIDENT	**$200**	WHO IS
DANCE-OBSESSED ARTISTS INCLUDE DEGAS & THIS FRENCH-MAN WHO TURNED TO CUTOUTS LATE IN LIFE	**$400**	WHO IS
IN NOVEMBER 1998 THE GETTY MUSEUM BOUGHT HIS SEMINAL 1870s PAINTING "IMPRESSION: SUNRISE"	**$600**	WHO IS
THIS 3-NAMED AMERI-CAN PAINTED POR-TRAITS OF FASHIONABLE SOCIETY & OF ROBERT LOUIS STEVENSON	**$800**	WHO IS
THIS 17th CENTURY SPANIARD CREATED THE INTRIGUING & COMPLEX PORTRAIT "LAS MENINAS"	**$1000**	WHO IS

DOUBLE JEOPARDY!

ART & ARTISTS

$200	WHO IS PAUL GAUGUIN?	**$200**
$400	WHO IS HENRI MATISSE?	**$400**
$600	WHO IS CLAUDE MONET?	**$600**
$800	WHO IS JOHN SINGER SARGENT?	**$800**
$1000	WHO IS DIEGO VELAZQUEZ?	**$1000**

126

DOUBLE JEOPARDY!

MICHELLE PFEIFFER PFILMS

TZIPPORAH, THE FUTURE BRIDE OF MOSES, WAS VOICE BY MICHELLE IN THIS 1998 ANIMATED FILM	**$200**	WHAT IS
ONE OF MICHELLE'S 2 FILMS WITH "DANGEROUS" IN THE TITLE	**$400**	WHAT IS
MICHELLE LIVENED UP THE LOUNGE ACT OF PIANO-PLAYING BROTHERS BEAU & JEFF BRIDGES IN THIS FILM	**$600**	WHAT IS
MICHELLE TRIES TO ESCAPE FROM THE MAFIA AFTER THE DEATH OF HER HIT-MAN HUSBAND IN THIS 1988 COMEDY	**$800**	WHAT IS
BOOK EDITOR JACK NICHOLSON GETS INTO SOME "HAIRY" SITUATIONS WITH MICHELLE IN THIS 1994 THRILLER	**$1000**	WHAT IS

DOUBLE JEOPARDY!

MICHELLE PFEIFFER PFILMS

$200	WHAT IS "THE PRINCE OF EGYPT"?	**$200**
$400	WHAT IS "DANGEROUS LIAISONS" OR "DANGEROUS MINDS"?	**$400**
$600	WHAT IS "THE FABULOUS BAKER BOYS"?	**$600**
$800	WHAT IS "MARRIED TO THE MOB"?	**$800**
$1000	WHAT IS "WOLF"?	**$1000**

FINAL JEOPARDY!

AVIATION

ON OCTOBER 14, 1997 HE
RE-CREATED A FEAT HE HAD
PERFORMED EXACTLY FIFTY
YEARS EARLIER

WHO IS

FINAL JEOPARDY!

AVIATION

WHO IS
CHARLES "CHUCK" YEAGER?

JEOPARDY!

TV THROUGH THE YEARS

IN JANUARY 1977 VIEWERS MET KUNTA KINTE & THE REST OF THE CHARACTERS IN THIS MINISERIES	**$100**	WHAT IS
RAY WALSTON PLAYED AN INVENTIVE ALIEN STRANDED ON EARTH IN THIS 1960s TV SITCOM HIT	**$200**	WHAT IS
WITH A BIT O' LUCK, SQUIRE, YOU'LL KNOW HE PLAYED CORPORAL PETER NEWKIRK ON "HOGAN'S HEROES"	**$300**	WHO IS
DAVID JAMES ELLIOTT OF "JAG" STARRED IN THE TV SERIES VERSION OF THIS 1987 KEVIN COSTNER FILM	**$400**	WHAT IS
GUNG-HO MAJOR JOHN D. MacGILLIS WAS THE SPIT-SHINED HEAD OF THE FAMILY ON THIS COMEDY FAVORITE	**$500**	WHAT IS

JEOPARDY!

TV THROUGH THE YEARS

$100 WHAT IS "ROOTS"? **$100**

$200 WHAT IS "MY FAVORITE MARTIAN"? **$200**

$300 WHO IS RICHARD DAWSON? **$300**

$400 WHAT IS "THE UNTOUCHABLES"? **$400**

$500 WHAT IS "MAJOR DAD"? **$500**

JEOPARDY!

FAMOUS FEUDS

GEORGE STEINBRENNER FIRED HIM 4 TIMES AS MANAGER OF THE YANKEES	**$100**	WHO IS
IN THE 1949 MOVIE "ROSEANNA McCOY", ROSEANNA RUNS OFF WITH A MEMBER OF THIS ENEMY FAMILY	**$200**	WHO ARE
THERE WAS NO LOVE LOST BETWEEN THESE 2 MEN, JFK'S VICE PRESIDENT & HIS ATTORNEY GENERAL	**$300**	WHO ARE
FROM THE LATIN FOR "TO AVENGE", THESE FAMILY FEUDS ARE ASSOCIATED WITH THE ISLAND OF CORSICA	**$400**	WHAT ARE
THE FUTURE LOUIS XI FEUDED WITH HIS FATHER WHILE HOLDING THIS FRENCH TITLE AS HEIR APPARENT	**$500**	WHAT IS

JEOPARDY!

FAMOUS FEUDS

$100	WHO IS BILLY MARTIN?	**$100**
$200	WHO ARE THE HATFIELDS?	**$200**
$300	WHO ARE LYNDON B. JOHNSON & ROBERT F. KENNEDY?	**$300**
$400	WHAT ARE VENDETTAS?	**$400**
$500	WHAT IS DAUPHIN?	**$500**

JEOPARDY!

COMMUNISM

THE POLICIES OF A GROUP OF COMMU-NISTS, OR THE PHONE CONNECTION OF A GROUP OF HOUSEHOLDS	**$100**	WHAT IS
"THE COMMUNIST MANIFESTO" DECLARES THAT THE HISTORY OF ALL SOCIETY IS THE HISTORY OF THESE STRUGGLES	**$200**	WHAT ARE
2-WORD NAME FOR THE COMMUNIST ARMY THAT BRUTALLY RULED CAMBODIA IN THE 1970s	**$300**	WHAT IS
ELECTED WITH BOTH COMMUNIST & SOCIALIST SUPPORT, HE WAS CHILE'S PRESIDENT FROM 1970 TO 1973	**$400**	WHO IS
SHORTENED FROM 2 RUSSIAN WORDS, IT WAS THE SUPREME POLICY-MAKING BODY IN THE USSR	**$500**	WHAT IS

JEOPARDY!

COMMUNISM

$100   WHAT IS THE PARTY LINE?   **$100**

$200   WHAT ARE CLASS STRUGGLES?   **$200**

$300   WHAT IS THE KHMER ROUGE?   **$300**

$400   WHO IS SALVADOR ALLENDE?   **$400**

$500   WHAT IS THE POLITBURO?   **$500**

JEOPARDY!

GOOD PROVERBS

OH, SHOOT! THIS IS "AS GOOD AS A MILE"	**$100**	WHAT IS
"ALL GOOD THINGS MUST" DO THIS	**$200**	WHAT IS
NOT BLACKTOP OR YELLOW BRICK, "THE ROAD TO HELL IS PAVED WITH" THESE	**$300**	WHAT ARE
BOY SCOUTS SHOULD HEED, "BIG WORDS SELDOM GO WITH GOOD" THESE	**$400**	WHAT ARE
"A GOOD START IS HALF" THIS	**$500**	WHAT IS

JEOPARDY!

GOOD PROVERBS

$100	WHAT IS "A MISS"?	**$100**
$200	WHAT IS "COME TO AN END"?	**$200**
$300	WHAT ARE "GOOD INTENTIONS"?	**$300**
$400	WHAT ARE "DEEDS"?	**$400**
$500	WHAT IS "THE RACE"?	**$500**

JEOPARDY!

FOR WHAT IT'S WORDSWORTH

"'TIS SAID, THAT SOME HAVE DIED FOR" THIS EMOTION	**$100**	WHAT IS
"THE RAINBOW COMES AND GOES, AND LOVELY IS" THIS FLOWER	**$200**	WHAT IS
"I WANDERED LONELY AS" ONE OF THESE, "THAT FLOATS ON HIGH O'ER VALES AND HILLS"	**$300**	WHAT IS
"O YE SPIRES OF" THIS UNIVERSITY TOWN! ... "YOUR PRESENCE OVERPOWERS THE SOBERNESS OF REASON"	**$400**	WHAT IS
"A FAMOUS MAN IS ROBIN HOOD, THE ENGLISH BALLAD-SINGER'S JOY! AND SCOTLAND HAS A THIEF AS GOOD", ... THIS OUTLAW	**$500**	WHO IS

JEOPARDY!

FOR WHAT IT'S WORDSWORTH

$100	WHAT IS "LOVE"?	$100
$200	WHAT IS "THE ROSE"?	$200
$300	WHAT IS "A CLOUD"?	$300
$400	WHAT IS OXFORD?	$400
$500	WHO IS ROB ROY?	$500

JEOPARDY!™

THE HUDSON RIVER

Clue	Value	Response
A BRIDGE NAMED FOR THIS FICTIONAL SNOOZER CROSSES THE HUDSON AT CATSKILL	$100	WHO IS
IN 1802 A MILITARY ACADEMY WAS ESTABLISHED AT THIS SITE	$200	WHAT IS
IN 1807 THE FIRST PRACTICAL STEAMBOAT, COMMONLY KNOWN BY THIS NAME, WAS LAUNCHED ON THE HUDSON	$300	WHAT IS
THIS INTERSTATE PARK ON THE HUDSON FEATURES 300- TO 500-FOOT-HIGH CLIFFS	$400	WHAT IS
IT WAS ON THIS SHIP THAT HENRY HUDSON WAS FIRST SENT UP THE RIVER	$500	WHAT IS

JEOPARDY!

THE HUDSON RIVER

$100	WHO IS RIP VAN WINKLE?	**$100**
$200	WHAT IS WEST POINT?	**$200**
$300	WHAT IS THE CLERMONT?	**$300**
$400	WHAT IS PALISADES INTERSTATE PARK?	**$400**
$500	WHAT IS THE HALF MOON?	**$500**

DOUBLE JEOPARDY!

IMMIGRANTS FROM RUSSIA

THE SECOND M IN MGM, THIS RUSSIAN IMMIGRANT CREATED THE STAR SYSTEM AS ONE OF THE HEADS OF THAT COMPANY	$200	WHO IS
THIS IMMIGRANT WAS A LONGTIME PRESIDENT OF RCA & ROSE TO BRIGADIER GENERAL DURING WWII	$400	WHO IS
IN THE 1940s HE & LINCOLN KIRSTEIN FOUNDED THE NEW YORK CITY BALLET	$600	WHO IS
THIS HELICOPTER PIONEER CAME TO THE U.S. SOON AFTER THE RUSSIAN REVOLUTION	$800	WHO IS
THE STORY OF THIS WOMAN WHO CO-WROTE "THE STORY OF CIVILIZATION" BEGAN IN RUSSIA IN 1898	$1000	WHO IS

DOUBLE JEOPARDY!

IMMIGRANTS FROM RUSSIA

$200 — WHO IS LOUIS B. MAYER? — **$200**

$400 — WHO IS DAVID SARNOFF? — **$400**

$600 — WHO IS GEORGE BALANCHINE? — **$600**

$800 — WHO IS IGOR SIKORSKY? — **$800**

$1000 — WHO IS ARIEL DURANT? — **$1000**

DOUBLE JEOPARDY!

JUNE SWOON

ONE OF THE 2 DAYS ON WHICH SUMMER CAN BEGIN IN THE NORTHERN HEMISPHERE	**$200**	WHAT ARE
THIS WAR BEGAN WITH AN ATTACK ACROSS THE 38th PARALLEL ON JUNE 25, 1950	**$400**	WHAT IS
AFTER A REVOLT IN ALGERIA, THIS MAN BECAME PREMIER OF FRANCE IN JUNE 1958 WITH ALMOST UNLIMITED AUTHORITY	**$600**	WHO IS
THE ROMANS NAMED THE MONTH FOR JUNO, PATRON GODDESS OF WOMEN & THIS SOCIAL RITE	**$800**	WHAT IS
ON JUNE 4 THIS COUNTRY HONORS CARL GUSTAF MANNER-HEIM, A LEADER IN ITS FIGHT FOR INDEPENDENCE FROM RUSSIA	**$1000**	WHAT IS

DOUBLE JEOPARDY!

JUNE SWOON

$200	WHAT ARE JUNE 21 OR JUNE 22?	$200
$400	WHAT IS THE KOREAN WAR?	$400
$600	WHO IS CHARLES DE GAULLE?	$600
$800	WHAT IS MARRIAGE?	$800
$1000	WHAT IS FINLAND?	$1000

DOUBLE JEOPARDY!

JACKSON ACTION

THIS GENERAL GAINED HIS FAMOUS NICKNAME AT THE FIRST BATTLE OF BULL RUN	**$200**	WHO IS
IN 1971 THIS BAPTIST MINISTER FOUNDED OPERATION PUSH (PEOPLE UNITED TO SAVE HUMANITY)	**$400**	WHO IS
"WHOA, NELLIE!" IS A CATCHPHRASE OF THIS LEGENDARY SPORTSCASTER	**$600**	WHO IS
THIS BRITISH ACTRESS & LABOUR POLITICIAN SAID, "ACTING IS NOT ABOUT DRESSING UP" BUT "ABOUT STRIPPING BARE"	**$800**	WHO IS
IN OCTOBER 1973 HE BECAME THE FIRST BLACK MAYOR OF ATLANTA, GEORGIA	**$1000**	WHO IS

DOUBLE JEOPARDY!

JACKSON ACTION

$200	WHO IS THOMAS "STONEWALL" JACKSON?	**$200**
$400	WHO IS JESSE JACKSON?	**$400**
$600	WHO IS KEITH JACKSON?	**$600**
$800	WHO IS GLENDA JACKSON?	**$800**
$1000	WHO IS MAYNARD JACKSON?	**$1000**

148

DOUBLE JEOPARDY!

CROSSWORD CLUES "G"

ZANE, OR LADY JANE (4)	**$200**	WHAT IS
"CONVENTION"AL SWISS CITY (6)	**$400**	WHAT IS
STYLE OF NOVELS, OR OF ARCHITECTURE (6)	**$600**	WHAT IS
SONDHEIM STRIPTEASE SHOW (5)	**$800**	WHAT IS
"MONSTER"-OUS RIVER (4)	**$1000**	WHAT IS

DOUBLE JEOPARDY!
CROSSWORD CLUES "G"

$200	WHAT IS GREY?	**$200**
$400	WHAT IS GENEVA?	**$400**
$600	WHAT IS GOTHIC?	**$600**
$800	WHAT IS "GYPSY"?	**$800**
$1000	WHAT IS GILA?	**$1000**

DOUBLE JEOPARDY!

PENINSULAS

THE REGION OF APULIA OCCUPIES THE "HEEL" OF THIS PENINSULA	**$200**	WHAT IS
COLOMBIA & VENEZUELA SHARE THE GUAJIRA PENINSULA, WHICH JUTS INTO THIS SEA	**$400**	WHAT IS
THE PENINSULA AT THE NORTHWESTERN EDGE OF THIS CONTINENT HAS BEEN CLAIMED BY ENGLAND, CHILE & ARGENTINA	**$600**	WHAT IS
MENTION THE EAST SIDE OF AUSTRALIA'S CAPE YORK PENINSULA & YOU'RE "REEF"ERRING TO THIS SEA	**$800**	WHAT IS
THE RAMONES SANG ABOUT THIS BEACH IN QUEENS THAT'S ON A PENINSULA OF THE SAME NAME	**$1000**	WHAT IS

DOUBLE JEOPARDY!

PENINSULAS

$200	WHAT IS THE ITALIAN PENINSULA? **$200**
$400	WHAT IS THE CARIBBEAN? **$400**
$600	WHAT IS ANTARCTICA? **$600**
$800	WHAT IS THE CORAL SEA? **$800**
$1000	WHAT IS ROCKAWAY BEACH? **$1000**

DOUBLE JEOPARDY!

MINIVANS

IN THE WORDS OF THE NEW YORK TIMES, THE MINIVAN "DETHRONED" THIS "AS THE PREFERRED UTILITY VEHICLE OF AMERICAN FAMILIES"	**$200**	WHAT IS
THIS NUMBER, THE USUAL MINIVAN PASSENGER CAPACITY, WOULD HAVE BEEN ENOUGH FOR TV'S BRADFORD CHILDREN	**$400**	WHAT IS
THE '96 DODGE CARAVAN WAS THE FIRST MINIVAN TO BE THIS "TREND"Y MAGAZINE'S CAR OF THE YEAR	**$600**	WHAT IS
ON NOV. 2, 1983 THIS MAN DROVE THE FIRST MODERN MINIVAN OFF A CHRYSLER ASSEMBLY LINE	**$800**	WHO IS
PERHAPS YOU CAN SAIL THE DARK EMERALD SEAS IN THIS HONDA MINIVAN THAT COMES IN DARK EMERALD PEARL	**$1000**	WHAT IS

DOUBLE JEOPARDY!

MINIVANS

$200	WHAT IS THE STATION WAGON?	**$200**
$400	WHAT IS 8?	**$400**
$600	WHAT IS MOTOR TREND?	**$600**
$800	WHO IS LEE IACOCCA?	**$800**
$1000	WHAT IS THE ODYSSEY?	**$1000**

FINAL JEOPARDY!
U.S. STATESMEN

IN 1814 & 1815, BEFORE HE
WAS PRESIDENT, HE SERVED
SIMULTANEOUSLY AS
SECRETARY OF STATE &
SECRETARY OF WAR

WHO IS

FINAL JEOPARDY!

U.S. STATESMEN

WHO IS
JAMES MONROE?

JEOPARDY!

MYTHS & MISSES

THIS GROUP OF WARRIORS CALLED HIPPOLYTA THEIR QUEEN	**$100**	WHO ARE
BY JOVE, SHE WAS RIGHT BY JUPITER, AS HIS WIFE	**$200**	WHO IS
ALL THAT BLOOMS OR THE ROMAN GODDESS OF ALL THAT BLOOMS	**$300**	WHO IS
PLATO SPLIT HER INTO 2 GODDESSES: ONE OF PURE LOVE & ONE OF COMMON LOVE	**$400**	WHO IS
ODYSSEUS SPENT A MONTH (OR MAYBE LONGER) WITH THIS SORCERESS ON THE ISLAND OF AEAEA	**$500**	WHO IS

JEOPARDY!

MYTHS & MISSES

$100 WHO ARE THE AMAZONS? $100

$200 WHO IS JUNO? $200

$300 WHO IS FLORA? $300

$400 WHO IS APHRODITE? $400

$500 WHO IS CIRCE? $500

JEOPARDY!

CHILDREN'S GAMES

YOU CAN PUT YOUR HANDS ON YOUR HEAD ONLY IF THIS PERSON "SAYS" THAT YOU CAN	**$100**	WHAT IS
PIECE OF EQUIPMENT YOU NEED TO PARTICIPATE IN A DOUBLE DUTCH TOURNAMENT	**$200**	WHAT IS
IT'S WHAT KIDS DO WITH THEIR HANDS WHILE RECITING, "MISS MARY, MACK, MACK, MACK, ALL DRESSED IN BLACK, BLACK, BLACK . . ."	**$300**	WHAT IS
AN EARLY FORM OF THIS PICK-UP GAME USED KNUCKLEBONES	**$400**	WHAT IS
IN THIS GAME THE SHOOTER MUST KNUCKLE DOWN WITH HIS GLASSIES	**$500**	WHAT IS

JEOPARDY!

CHILDREN'S GAMES

$100	WHO IS SIMON?	**$100**
$200	WHAT IS A (JUMP) ROPE?	**$200**
$300	WHAT IS CLAP THEM?	**$300**
$400	WHAT IS JACKS?	**$400**
$500	WHAT IS MARBLES?	**$500**

JEOPARDY!

STARS

Clue	Value	Response
HIS LATER CAREER INCLUDED INTONING THAT PAUL MASSON WOULD "SELL NO WINE BEFORE ITS TIME"	$100	WHO IS
THIS ACTRESS IS THE SISTER OF ACTORS ROSANNA, DAVID & ALEXIS	$200	WHO IS
AFTER A 1980 CONTRACT DISPUTE, THIS ACTRESS ONLY APPEARED IN "THREE'S COMPANY" TALKING ON THE PHONE	$300	WHO IS
HAVING EMERGED AS A STAR IN "APOLLO 13" & "TWISTER", HE GETS CONFUSED WITH BILL PULLMAN LESS OFTEN	$400	WHO IS
THIS ACTOR, THE MAD HATTER ON "BATMAN", WASN'T RELATED TO "THE DUKE"	$500	WHO IS

JEOPARDY!

STARS

$100 WHO IS ORSON WELLES? **$100**

$200 WHO IS PATRICIA ARQUETTE? **$200**

$300 WHO IS SUZANNE SOMERS? **$300**

$400 WHO IS BILL PAXTON? **$400**

$500 WHO IS DAVID WAYNE? **$500**

JEOPARDY!

PHYSICAL SCIENCE

Clue	Value	Response
SOLID WATER IS ICE; SOLID CARBON DIOXIDE HAS THIS 2-WORD NAME	**$100**	WHAT IS
ALSO CALLED ZYMOSIS, THIS ACTION INVOLVING ENZYMES PRODUCES BEER & CHEESE	**$200**	WHAT IS
A PHONON IS A TINY PACKET OF SOUND; CHANGE 1 LETTER TO GET THIS UNIT OF ELECTROMAGNETIC ENERGY	**$300**	WHAT IS
THIS SYNONYM FOR "BURNING" IS THE NAME OF A "CHAMBER" WHERE ROCKETS BURN FUEL	**$400**	WHAT IS
A MILLIMETER OF THIS ELEMENT IS A COMMON UNIT FOR MEASURING PRESSURE, INCLUDING BLOOD PRESSURE	**$500**	WHAT IS

JEOPARDY!

PHYSICAL SCIENCE

$100	WHAT IS DRY ICE?	**$100**
$200	WHAT IS FERMENTATION?	**$200**
$300	WHAT IS A PHOTON?	**$300**
$400	WHAT IS COMBUSTION?	**$400**
$500	WHAT IS MERCURY?	**$500**

JEOPARDY!

GANGSTER'S DICTIONARY

I HATES IT WHEN THE COPS PUTS THESE "BRACELETS" ON ME AFTER A BUST	$100	WHAT ARE
YOU MUGS, I NEEDS A "CAN OPENER", A TOOL USED TO OPEN ONE OF THESE, NOT A TIN CAN	$200	WHAT IS
ROLL OUT THESE "BONES", BOYS, SO WE CAN PLAY SOME GAMES OF CHANCE	$300	WHAT ARE
ONE DAY I MIGHT GO LEGIT & GET A CUSH JOB AS A "GUMSHOE", A PRIVATE ONE OF THESE	$400	WHAT IS
KEEP YOUR HEAD LOW ... I JUST SAW A "SALT & PEPPER", ONE OF THESE, GO BY	$500	WHAT IS

JEOPARDY!

GANGSTER'S DICTIONARY

$100	WHAT ARE HANDCUFFS?	**$100**
$200	WHAT IS A SAFE?	**$200**
$300	WHAT ARE DICE?	**$300**
$400	WHAT IS A DETECTIVE?	**$400**
$500	WHAT IS A POLICE CAR?	**$500**

JEOPARDY!

THE '60s

THIS AMERICAN WENT INTO SPACE BEFORE KENNEDY MADE HIS "LET'S PUT A MAN ON THE MOON" SPEECH	**$100**	WHO IS
LACK OF PUBLIC DEMAND LED THE U.S. TREASURY TO OFFICIALLY DIS-CONTINUE THESE BILLS AUGUST 10, 1966	**$200**	WHAT ARE
SWORN IN MARCH 17, 1969, SHE SAID SHE'D PUSH FOR FACE-TO-FACE TALKS WITH THE ARABS	**$300**	WHO IS
MARTIN LUTHER KING JR.'S FREEDOM WALK IN 1965 SPANNED THE 50 MILES BETWEEN THESE 2 ALABAMA CITIES	**$400**	WHAT ARE
IN FEBRUARY 1960 A MEMBER OF THIS BREWING FAMILY WAS KIDNAPPED IN COLORADO	**$500**	WHAT IS

JEOPARDY!

THE '60s

$100	WHO IS ALAN SHEPARD (JR.)?
$200	WHAT ARE $2 BILLS?
$300	WHO IS GOLDA MEIR?
$400	WHAT ARE SELMA & MONTGOMERY?
$500	WHAT IS THE COORS FAMILY?

DOUBLE JEOPARDY!

OXYMORONS

NAME OF A MOTOR-CYCLE GANG FOUNDED IN CALIFORNIA IN 1948; WHAT DO THEIR WINGS LOOK LIKE?	**$200**	WHAT ARE
PSYCHOLOGISTS PUT IT BEFORE "AGGRESSIVE" TO DESCRIBE BEHAVIOR LIKE SULKING & PROCRASTINATION	**$400**	WHAT IS
"SAME" THIS IS A SLANGY RESPONSE ON BEING GIVEN IRRELE-VANT INFORMATION	**$600**	WHAT IS
FRENCH KING HENRY IV CALLED ENGLISH KING JAMES I "THE WISEST" ONE OF THESE "IN CHRISTENDOM"	**$800**	WHAT IS
SHH! A 1994 SHORT STORY COLLECTION BY ALICE MUNRO IS TITLED "OPEN" THESE	**$1000**	WHAT ARE

DOUBLE JEOPARDY!

OXYMORONS

$200	WHAT ARE THE HELL'S ANGELS?	**$200**
$400	WHAT IS PASSIVE?	**$400**
$600	WHAT IS DIFFERENCE?	**$600**
$800	WHAT IS "FOOL"?	**$800**
$1000	WHAT ARE SECRETS?	**$1000**

DOUBLE JEOPARDY!

GEOGRAPHY

Clue	Value	Response
THIS COUNTRY'S LONGEST FJORD, SOGNE FJORD, EXTENDS 127 MILES INLAND	**$200**	WHAT IS
CAPE BABA, THE WESTERNMOST POINT OF THIS CONTINENT, JUTS INTO THE AEGEAN SEA	**$400**	WHAT IS
THE SEINE RIVER RISES ON THE PLATEAU OF LANGRES NEAR THIS MUSTARD CAPITAL	**$600**	WHAT IS
IN 1610 THE DUTCH EAST INDIA COMPANY BUILT A TRADING POST IN THIS CITY; 9 YEARS LATER THEY NAMED IT BATAVIA	**$800**	WHAT IS
THIS COUNTRY'S DECCAN PLATEAU LIES BETWEEN THE EASTERN & WESTERN GHATS RANGES	**$1000**	WHAT IS

DOUBLE JEOPARDY!

GEOGRAPHY

$200	WHAT IS NORWAY?	**$200**
$400	WHAT IS ASIA?	**$400**
$600	WHAT IS DIJON?	**$600**
$800	WHAT IS JAKARTA?	**$800**
$1000	WHAT IS INDIA?	**$1000**

172

DOUBLE JEOPARDY!

RAILROAD TERMS

THE PERSON IN THIS POST SUPERVISES THE TRAIN CREW & COLLECTS FARES	**$200**	WHAT IS
THIS TERM FOR PORTERS CAME FROM THEIR COLORFUL HEADGEAR	**$400**	WHAT ARE
IT'S A FIREBOX FEEDER, AN APPRENTICE TO THE ENGINEER, OR A FAMOUS BRAM	**$600**	WHAT IS
A TRACK INSPECTOR, WHETHER OR NOT HE'S FROM WICHITA	**$800**	WHAT IS
A PIN PULLER OPERATES THESE IN THE YARD, TO SHUNT CARS FROM ONE TRACK TO ANOTHER	**$1000**	WHAT ARE

DOUBLE JEOPARDY!

RAILROAD TERMS

$200	WHAT IS THE CONDUCTOR?	**$200**
$400	WHAT ARE REDCAPS?	**$400**
$600	WHAT IS A STOKER?	**$600**
$800	WHAT IS A LINEMAN?	**$800**
$1000	WHAT ARE SWITCHES?	**$1000**

DOUBLE JEOPARDY!

THEATRE

Clue	Value	Response
IN 1999 BRIAN DENNEHY PLAYED WILLY LOMAN ON BROADWAY IN A 50th ANNIVERSARY PRODUCTION OF THIS PLAY	**$200**	WHAT IS
A RITZY NEW YORK HOTEL PROVIDES THE SETTING FOR THIS PROGRAM OF 3 1-ACT COMEDIES BY NEIL SIMON	**$400**	WHAT IS
LEAPIN' LIZARDS! THIS TENNESSEE WILLIAMS PLAY TAKES PLACE AT THE COSTA VERDE RESORT IN MEXICO	**$600**	WHAT IS
PART 1 OF "MURDER IN THE CATHEDRAL" BEGINS WITH THE RETURN OF THIS ARCHBISHOP AFTER 7 YEARS IN EXILE	**$800**	WHO IS
MALICIOUS RUMORS RUIN THE LIVES OF 2 TEACHERS IN THIS LILLIAN HELLMAN PLAY	**$1000**	WHAT IS

DOUBLE JEOPARDY!

THEATRE

$200	WHAT IS "DEATH OF A SALESMAN"?	$200
$400	WHAT IS "PLAZA SUITE"?	$400
$600	WHAT IS "THE NIGHT OF THE IGUANA"?	$600
$800	WHO IS THOMAS (A) BECKET?	$800
$1000	WHAT IS "THE CHILDREN'S HOUR"?	$1000

DOUBLE JEOPARDY!

SPORTS

Clue	Value	Response
THEY'RE THE MAIN CROSSTOWN RIVAL OF UCLA's BRUINS	$200	WHO ARE
THIS "BIG UNIT" BROKE INTO THE MAJORS WITH MONTREAL IN 1988, STRIKING OUT 25 BATTERS IN 26 INNINGS	$400	WHO IS
THE LOGO OF THIS CITY'S NHL TEAM IS A WINGED CAR TIRE	$600	WHAT IS
PETE SAMPRAS DEFEATED THIS AUSSIE TO WIN WIMBLEDON IN 2000	$800	WHO IS
NICKNAMED "THE BIG O", HE WAS THE NBA's ROOKIE OF THE YEAR FOR THE 1960–61 SEASON	$1000	WHO IS

DOUBLE JEOPARDY!

SPORTS

$200	WHO ARE THE USC TROJANS?	**$200**
$400	WHO IS RANDY JOHNSON?	**$400**
$600	WHAT IS DETROIT?	**$600**
$800	WHO IS PATRICK RAFTER?	**$800**
$1000	WHO IS OSCAR ROBERTSON?	**$1000**

DOUBLE JEOPARDY!

THE BIRTH OF WORDS

THIS SCOTTISH ENTREE MAY DERIVE ITS NAME FROM THE OLD FRENCH HAGUIER, "TO CHOP"	**$200**	WHAT IS
POSSIBLY FROM THE LATIN FOR "FAREWELL TO MEAT", IT'S A TIME OF PRE-LENTEN MERRYMAKING	**$400**	WHAT IS
THIS TERM FOR A STEAMING HOT SPRING COMES FROM THE NAME OF A FAMOUS ICELANDIC HOT SPRING	**$600**	WHAT IS
FROM THE OLD SLAVIC FOR "SLAVE", THIS WORD ENTERED THE LANGUAGE FROM KAREL CAPEK'S 1921 PLAY "R.U.R."	**$800**	WHAT IS
THIS ITALIAN-SOUNDING NAME FOR A SEDUCER COMES FROM THE 1703 PLAY "THE FAIR PENITENT"	**$1000**	WHAT IS

DOUBLE JEOPARDY!

THE BIRTH OF WORDS

$200	WHAT IS HAGGIS?	$200
$400	WHAT IS CARNIVAL?	$400
$600	WHAT IS A GEYSER?	$600
$800	WHAT IS ROBOT?	$800
$1000	WHAT IS LOTHARIO?	$1000

FINAL JEOPARDY!

U.S. GOVERNMENT

LAWRENCE WALSH &
DONALD SMALTZ
HELD THIS JOB CREATED
BY 1978's ETHICS IN
GOVERNMENT ACT

WHAT IS

FINAL JEOPARDY!
U.S. GOVERNMENT

WHAT IS
INDEPENDENT COUNSEL
(OR SPECIAL PROSECUTOR)?

JEOPARDY!

SUMMER

1935 FOLK OPERA THAT FEATURED THE SONG "SUMMERTIME"	**$100**	WHAT IS
1 OF THE 2 MONTHS IN THE U.S. IN WHICH AN "INDIAN SUMMER" MAY OCCUR	**$200**	WHAT IS
AS SUMMER QUINN, NICOLE EGGERT SAVED LIVES ON THIS INTERNATIONALLY SYNDICATED SERIES	**$300**	WHAT IS
THIS COUNTRY HOSTED THE SUMMER OLYMPIC GAMES ONLY ONCE, IN 1896	**$400**	WHAT IS
THE SUMMER ONE OF THESE IS IN PUSHKIN; THE WINTER ONE IS NORTH OF IT IN ST. PETERSBURG	**$500**	WHAT IS

JEOPARDY!

SUMMER

$100	WHAT IS "PORGY AND BESS"?	$100
$200	WHAT IS OCTOBER OR NOVEMBER?	$200
$300	WHAT IS "BAYWATCH"?	$300
$400	WHAT IS GREECE?	$400
$500	WHAT IS A PALACE?	$500

JEOPARDY!

WORLDLY WISDOM

Clue	Value	Response
LOCALLY, THE WORLD CAPITAL IS SPELLED W-I-E-N	**$100**	WHAT IS
THE STRATEGIC IMPORTANCE OF THE BLACK SEA IS NOT LOST ON THIS COUNTRY THAT OCCUPIES ITS SOUTHERN RIM	**$200**	WHAT IS
YOU'LL FIND REINDEER LAKE COVERING OVER 2,400 SQUARE MILES IN THIS COUNTY	**$300**	WHAT IS
LOCATED IN THE SOUTHWESTERN PART OF THE CONTINENT, IT'S THE SECOND-LARGEST DESERT IN AFRICA	**$400**	WHAT IS
UKRAINE, GERMANY & THE BALTIC SEA ALL BORDER THIS COUNTRY	**$500**	WHAT IS

185

JEOPARDY!

WORLDLY WISDOM

$100	WHAT IS VIENNA?	$100
$200	WHAT IS TURKEY?	$200
$300	WHAT IS CANADA?	$300
$400	WHAT IS THE KALAHARI?	$400
$500	WHAT IS POLAND?	$500

JEOPARDY!

WE LOVE LUCY

Clue	Value	Response
LUCY & RICKY'S NEW YORK LANDLORDS	$100	WHO ARE
LUCY RICARDO'S MAIDEN NAME, MacGILLICUDDY, REFLECTED HER FICTIONAL ANCESTRY IN THIS COUNTRY	$200	WHAT IS
OF 1950, 1953 OR 1956, THE YEAR OF LITTLE RICKY'S "BIRTH" & DESI ARNAZ JR.'S BIRTH	$300	WHAT IS
IN ONE EPISODE, LUCY TRIES TO STEAL THE CEMENT BLOCK WITH THIS ACTOR'S FOOT-PRINTS IN IT AS A SOUVENIR	$400	WHO IS
RICKY RICARDO WAS A BANDLEADER AT THE TROPICANA CLUB & THIS ONE	$500	WHAT IS

JEOPARDY!

WE LOVE LUCY

$100 WHO ARE FRED & ETHEL MERTZ? **$100**

$200 WHAT IS SCOTLAND? **$200**

$300 WHAT IS 1953? **$300**

$400 WHO IS JOHN WAYNE? **$400**

$500 WHAT IS THE BABALU CLUB? **$500**

JEOPARDY!™

THE ANIMAL KINGDOM

THE SIBERIAN SPECIES OF THIS CARNIVORE IS THE LARGEST CAT	**$100**	WHAT IS
UNLIKE MOST LIZARDS, THIS COLOR-CHANGING LIZARD HAS FEET THAT GRASP LIKE HANDS RATHER THAN CLING WITH CLAWS	**$200**	WHAT IS
WHEN ALARMED, THIS SECOND-LARGEST RODENT SMACKS ITS BROAD, FLAT TAIL AGAINST THE WATER	**$300**	WHAT IS
THE PILOT WHALE IS ONE OF THE LARGER MEMBERS OF THIS FAMILY OF MAMMALS	**$400**	WHAT ARE
THE NAME OF THIS CLASS OF MOLLUSKS COMES FROM THE GREEK FOR "BELLY FOOT"	**$500**	WHAT IS

JEOPARDY!

THE ANIMAL KINGDOM

$100 WHAT IS THE TIGER? **$100**

$200 WHAT IS THE CHAMELEON? **$200**

$300 WHAT IS THE BEAVER? **$300**

$400 WHAT ARE DOLPHINS? **$400**

$500 WHAT IS GASTROPODA? **$500**

JEOPARDY!

THE NAME'S FAMILIAR

IBERIA IS AN AIRLINE BASED IN THIS COUNTRY	**$100**	WHAT IS
LANDSEER'S LIONS ARE AT THE BASE OF NELSON'S COLUMN IN THIS SQUARE	**$200**	WHAT IS
IN THE 1960s MICHAEL ABDUL MALIK OF THE U.K. & MALCOLM LITTLE OF THE U.S. BOTH USED THIS AS THEIR LAST NAME	**$300**	WHAT IS
TRADITIONAL MEMBER OF THE MAGI WHOSE NAME IS ALSO A MEASURE EQUAL TO 16 REGULAR BOTTLES OF CHAMPAGNE	**$400**	WHO IS
LAST NAME OF JULIAN, UNESCO's FIRST DIRECTOR-GENERAL; HE WAS THE BROTHER OF WRITER ALDOUS	**$500**	WHAT IS

JEOPARDY!

THE NAME'S FAMILIAR

$100 | WHAT IS SPAIN? | $100

$200 | WHAT IS TRAFALGAR SQUARE? | $200

$300 | WHAT IS X? | $300

$400 | WHO IS BALTHAZAR? | $400

$500 | WHAT IS HUXLEY? | $500

JEOPARDY!

"BOR"ING

Clue	Value	Response
A RECENT CONVERT TO CHRISTIANITY OR ONE WITH A RENEWED FAITH IS DESCRIBED AS THIS	$100	WHAT IS
YOU'LL FIND THE MEDOC, SAUTERNES & SOME GRAND CHATEAUX IN THIS REGION OF FRANCE	$200	WHAT IS
THIS TERM FOR A HOUSE OF ILL REPUTE GOES BACK TO THE 16th CENTURY	$300	WHAT IS
ISLAND IN THE SOUTH CHINA SEA ON WHICH YOU'D FIND BRUNEI & PART OF INDONESIA	$400	WHAT IS
HE CIRCLED THE EARTH IN 1965 & CIRCLED THE MOON IN 1968	$500	WHO IS

JEOPARDY!

"BOR"ING

$100   WHAT IS BORN AGAIN? $100

$200   WHAT IS BORDEAUX? $200

$300   WHAT IS BORDELLO? $300

$400   WHAT IS BORNEO? $400

$500   WHO IS FRANK BORMAN? $500

DOUBLE JEOPARDY!

CLASSICAL COMPOSERS

HIS "WILLIAM TELL" WAS TO HAVE BEEN THE FIRST OF 5 OPERAS FOR THE PARIS OPERA BUT HIS CONTRACT WAS SET ASIDE	**$200**	WHO IS
IN WEIMAR HE WROTE A SET OF ORGAN CHORALES FOR HIS "ORGELBUCHLEIN", OR "LITTLE ORGAN BOOK"	**$400**	WHO IS
IN 1939 THE HELSINKI MUSIC INSTITUTE CHANGED ITS NAME TO HONOR THIS FAMED GRADUATE	**$600**	WHO IS
HIS 1905 COMPOSITION "LA MER" WAS INSPIRED BY THE IDEAS OF PAINTERS	**$800**	WHO IS
IN 1907 HE BECAME PROFESSOR OF PIANO AT THE ROYAL ACADEMY OF MUSIC IN BUDAPEST	**$1000**	WHO IS

DOUBLE JEOPARDY!

CLASSICAL COMPOSERS

$200	WHO IS GIOACCHINO ROSSINI?	$200
$400	WHO IS JOHANN SEBASTIAN BACH?	$400
$600	WHO IS JEAN SIBELIUS?	$600
$800	WHO IS CLAUDE DEBUSSY?	$800
$1000	WHO IS BELA BARTOK?	$1000

DOUBLE JEOPARDY!

FOOD

THIS PRESERVE WAS ORIGINALLY MADE FROM QUINCE; SEVILLE ORANGES ARE NOW NORMALLY USED	$200	WHAT IS
A TRADITIONAL ACCOMPANIMENT FOR FRIED CATFISH, THESE CORNMEAL DUMPLINGS ARE FLAVORED WITH CHOPPED SCALLIONS	$400	WHAT ARE
THIS GROUND BEEF PATTY FLAVORED WITH MINCED ONION & SEASONINGS WAS NAMED FOR A 19th CENTURY PHYSICIAN	$600	WHAT IS
THESE POTATO PANCAKES ARE A TRADITIONAL HANUKKAH DISH	$800	WHAT ARE
IT'S THE WHITMAN, MASSACHUSETTS INN WHERE THE CHOCOLATE CHIP COOKIE WAS CREATED IN THE 1930s	$1000	WHAT IS

DOUBLE JEOPARDY!

FOOD

$200	WHAT IS MARMALADE?	**$200**
$400	WHAT ARE HUSHPUPPIES?	**$400**
$600	WHAT IS SALISBURY STEAK?	**$600**
$800	WHAT ARE LATKES?	**$800**
$1000	WHAT IS THE TOLL HOUSE INN?	**$1000**

DOUBLE JEOPARDY!

MEDICAL ABBREV.

IT CAN SAVE SOMEONE'S LIFE: CPR	**$200**	WHAT IS
A TYPE OF MANAGED CARE PLAN: HMO	**$400**	WHAT IS
IT RECORDS BRAIN WAVES: EEG	**$600**	WHAT IS
ONE WHO TAKES CARE OF THE SICK: LPN	**$800**	WHAT IS
A VACCINATION: DPT	**$1000**	WHAT IS

DOUBLE JEOPARDY!

MEDICAL ABBREV.

$200	WHAT IS CARDIOPULMONARY RESUSCITATION?	$200
$400	WHAT IS HEALTH MAINTENANCE ORGANIZATION?	$400
$600	WHAT IS ELECTRO-ENCEPHALOGRAPH (OR ...GRAM)?	$600
$800	WHAT IS LICENSED PRACTICAL NURSE?	$800
$1000	WHAT IS DIPHTHERIA-PERTUSSIS-TETANUS?	$1000

200

DOUBLE JEOPARDY!

DIRECTORS & FILMS

HE GOT HIS OSKAR FOR "SCHINDLER'S LIST"	**$200**	WHO IS
HE PLAYED JOHN REED IN "REDS"	**$400**	WHO IS
HE DIRECTED HIS DAD WALTER IN "TREASURE OF THE SIERRA MADRE"	**$600**	WHO IS
"YOU CAN'T TAKE IT WITH YOU" WAS ONE OF HIS LESS CORNY EFFORTS	**$800**	WHO IS
BRITISH KNIGHT WHO DIRECTED "GANDHI"	**$1000**	WHO IS

DOUBLE JEOPARDY!

DIRECTORS & FILMS

$200	WHO IS STEVEN SPIELBERG?	$200
$400	WHO IS WARREN BEATTY?	$400
$600	WHO IS JOHN HUSTON?	$600
$800	WHO IS FRANK CAPRA?	$800
$1000	WHO IS (SIR) RICHARD ATTENBOROUGH?	$1000

DOUBLE JEOPARDY!

GOING DUTCH

IN HER DIARY SHE WROTE, "IT IS NOT THE DUTCH PEOPLE'S FAULT THAT WE ARE HAVING SUCH A MISERABLE TIME"	**$200**	WHO IS
JOHAN CRUYFF, KNOWN AS THE DUTCH MASTER, WAS TOPS IN THIS SPORT & EVEN PLAYED FOR THE L.A. AZTECS	**$400**	WHAT IS
IN 1993 NORTHWEST AIRLINES FORMED AN ALLIANCE WITH THIS DUTCH COMPANY	**$600**	WHAT IS
THE ROOTS OF THIS U.S. STATE CAPITAL GO BACK TO FORT NASSAU, A TRADING POST FOUNDED BY THE DUTCH IN 1614	**$800**	WHAT IS
A NEW WATERWAY OPENED IN 1872 ALLOWED LARGE VESSELS PASSAGE TO THIS DUTCH CITY, NOW A TOP WORLD PORT	**$1000**	WHAT IS

DOUBLE JEOPARDY!

GOING DUTCH

$200	WHO IS ANNE FRANK? **$200**
$400	WHAT IS SOCCER? **$400**
$600	WHAT IS KLM (ROYAL DUTCH AIRLINES)? **$600**
$800	WHAT IS ALBANY (NEW YORK)? **$800**
$1000	WHAT IS ROTTERDAM? **$1000**

DOUBLE JEOPARDY!

WHICH CAME FIRST?

TEXAS STATEHOOD, NORTH DAKOTA STATEHOOD, MICHIGAN STATEHOOD	**$200**	WHAT IS
HADRIAN'S WALL, THE WAILING WALL, THE BERLIN WALL	**$400**	WHAT IS
"THE TEMPEST", "ROMEO AND JULIET", "MACBETH"	**$600**	WHAT IS
TAFT-HARTLEY ACT, VOTING RIGHTS ACT, SHERMAN ANTITRUST ACT	**$800**	WHAT IS
BYZANTIUM FALLS TO THE TURKS, SALADIN CAPTURES JERUSALEM, CORNWALLIS SURRENDERS AT YORKTOWN	**$1000**	WHAT IS

DOUBLE JEOPARDY!

WHICH CAME FIRST?

$200	WHAT IS MICHIGAN STATEHOOD?	**$200**
$400	WHAT IS THE WAILING WALL?	**$400**
$600	WHAT IS "ROMEO AND JULIET"?	**$600**
$800	WHAT IS THE SHERMAN ANTITRUST ACT?	**$800**
$1000	WHAT IS SALADIN CAPTURES JERUSALEM?	**$1000**

FINAL JEOPARDY!
QUOTABLE DEFINITIONS

TED HUGHES WROTE THAT
IT'S WHERE A CHILD CAN
SIT "WITH THE GENIUS
OF THE EARTH"

WHERE IS

FINAL JEOPARDY!
QUOTABLE DEFINITIONS

WHERE IS
IN THE LIBRARY?

JEOPARDY!

AMERICANA

A LITERARY MAGAZINE EDITED BY O. HENRY IN 1894, OR A ROCK MAGAZINE FOUNDED IN 1967	**$100**	WHAT IS
POP MOMAND CALLED HIS NEW COMIC STRIP IN 1913 "KEEPING UP WITH" THIS FAMILY	**$200**	WHO ARE
A CONFEDERATE CAMP FIRE SONG ABOUT "EATING" THESE (i.e. PEANUTS) CALLED THEM "GOODNESS HOW DELICIOUS"	**$300**	WHAT ARE
THE FIRST MISS AMERICA HE CROWNED WAS LEE MERIWETHER IN 1954	**$400**	WHO IS
IT WAS INCORPORATED AS A CITY MAY 3, 1802 WITH ITS MAYOR TO BE APPOINTED BY THE PRESIDENT	**$500**	WHAT IS

JEOPARDY!

AMERICANA

$100 WHAT IS ROLLING STONE? **$100**

$200 WHO ARE THE JONESES? **$200**

$300 WHAT ARE GOOBER PEAS? **$300**

$400 WHO IS BERT PARKS? **$400**

$500 WHAT IS WASHINGTON, D.C.? **$500**

JEOPARDY!

"WHIP"s & "CHAIN"s

IT'S A SERIES OF POSITIONS IN WHICH EACH ONE HAS DIRECT AUTHORITY OVER THE ONE IMMEDIATELY BELOW	$100	WHAT IS
SENATE POSITION HELD BY NEVADA DEMOCRAT HARRY REID	$200	WHAT IS
THIS NORTH AMERICAN BIRD IS NAMED FOR ITS ODD CALL, WHICH IT MAY REPEAT SEVERAL HUNDRED TIMES WITHOUT STOPPING	$300	WHAT IS
TOOL PREFERRED BY LEATHERFACE IN A 1974 HORROR CLASSIC	$400	WHAT IS
"A SANDWICH JUST ISN'T A SANDWICH WITHOUT" THE "TANGY ZIP" OF THIS KRAFT SALAD DRESSING	$500	WHAT IS

JEOPARDY!

"WHIP"s & "CHAIN"s

$100	WHAT IS CHAIN OF COMMAND?	$100
$200	WHAT IS MINORITY WHIP?	$200
$300	WHAT IS THE WHIPPOORWILL?	$300
$400	WHAT IS A CHAINSAW?	$400
$500	WHAT IS MIRACLE WHIP?	$500

JEOPARDY!

WHAT'S THE MATTER ... YELLOW??

APPROPRIATELY, YOU CAN SEE THE YELLOW-BELLIED MARMOT IN THIS WYOMING-MONTANA-IDAHO NATIONAL PARK	**$100**	WHAT IS
THE YELLOW-WINGED TYPE OF THIS MAMMAL HOPES INSECTS DON'T SEE ITS YELLOW WINGS COMING	**$200**	WHAT IS
CALL IT CRAZY, BUT UNLIKE OTHER TYPES OF THESE BIRDS, THE YELLOW-BILLED ONE BUILDS ITS OWN NEST INSTEAD OF INVADING	**$300**	WHAT IS
NARCISSUS PSEUDO-NARCISSUS IS THE SCIENTIFIC NAME OF THIS STRIKING YELLOW FLOWER	**$400**	WHAT IS
EAST AFRICA IS HOME TO THE YELLOW SPECIES OF THESE LARGE MONKEYS KNOWN FOR THEIR COLORFUL BOTTOMS	**$500**	WHAT ARE

JEOPARDY!

WHAT'S THE MATTER ... YELLOW??

$100 — WHAT IS YELLOWSTONE? — $100

$200 — WHAT IS THE BAT? — $200

$300 — WHAT IS THE CUCKOO? — $300

$400 — WHAT IS THE DAFFODIL? — $400

$500 — WHAT ARE BABOONS? — $500

JEOPARDY!

PEOPLE IN HISTORY

Clue	Value	Response
THIS FIRST U.S. FIRST LADY, A FINE EQUESTRIENNE, ONCE RODE A HORSE UP THE STAIRS OF HER UNCLE'S HOUSE	$100	WHO IS
INDIA'S 5th CENTURY PLAYWRIGHT KALIDASA WROTE HIS MASTERPIECE, "SHAKUNTALA", IN THIS CLASSICAL LANGUAGE	$200	WHAT IS
HE WAS CONDEMNED, BUT NOT CENSURED, BY THE SENATE IN DECEMBER 1954	$300	WHO IS
THE LAST KING WILLIAM TO RULE ENGLAND HAD THIS NUMBER AFTER HIS NAME	$400	WHAT IS
HE WAS CHIEF MINISTER OF FRANCE FROM 1624 TO 1642	$500	WHO IS

JEOPARDY!

PEOPLE IN HISTORY

$100 — WHO IS MARTHA WASHINGTON? — $100

$200 — WHAT IS SANSKRIT? — $200

$300 — WHO IS JOSEPH McCARTHY? — $300

$400 — WHAT IS IV? — $400

$500 — WHO IS CARDINAL RICHELIEU? — $500

JEOPARDY!

LITERATURE

PROFESSOR BHAER IN HER BOOK "LITTLE WOMEN" WAS PARTLY BASED ON RALPH WALDO EMERSON	**$100**	WHO IS
THE POEMS OF SCOTLAND'S ROBERT FERGUSSON, WHO DIED INSANE AT AGE 24, INFLUENCED THIS "TAM O'SHANTER" POET	**$200**	WHO IS
THIS BORIS PASTERNAK BESTSELLER WASN'T PUBLISHED IN THE USSR UNTIL 40 YEARS AFTER IT WAS WRITTEN	**$300**	WHAT IS
SHE SET HER 1931 NOVEL "SHADOWS ON THE ROCK" IN QUEBEC, NOT IN NEBRASKA	**$400**	WHO IS
ALFRED VENISON WAS A PSEUDONYM OF THIS "CANTOS" POET & FASCIST SYMPATHIZER	**$500**	WHO IS

JEOPARDY!

LITERATURE

$100	WHO IS LOUISA MAY ALCOTT?	$100
$200	WHO IS ROBERT BURNS?	$200
$300	WHAT IS "DOCTOR ZHIVAGO"?	$300
$400	WHO IS WILLA CATHER?	$400
$500	WHO IS EZRA POUND?	$500

JEOPARDY!

DEREK JETER

IN 2000 DEREK BECAME THE FIRST YANKEE EVER NAMED MVP OF THIS ANNUAL GAME	$100	WHAT IS
DEREK REPORTEDLY BEGAN A ROMANCE WITH THIS CHART-TOPPING SINGER AFTER MEETING HER AT A FRESH AIR FUND EVENT	$200	WHO IS
IN THE YANKEES' 1998 & 1999 WORLD SERIES SWEEPS OF THESE 2 TEAMS, DEREK HIT IN ALL 8 GAMES	$300	WHAT ARE
DEREK WENT TO HIGH SCHOOL IN THIS MICHIGAN CITY, & PROBABLY HAD A GAL THERE; MAYBE MORE THAN ONE	$400	WHAT IS
DEREK'S ABOUT A YEAR YOUNGER THAN THIS RED SOX SHORTSTOP WITH WHOM HE'S OFTEN COMPARED	$500	WHO IS

JEOPARDY!

DEREK JETER

$100	WHAT IS THE ALL-STAR GAME?	**$100**
$200	WHO IS MARIAH CAREY?	**$200**
$300	WHAT ARE THE ATLANTA BRAVES & SAN DIEGO PADRES?	**$300**
$400	WHAT IS KALAMAZOO?	**$400**
$500	WHO IS NOMAR GARCIAPARRA?	**$500**

DOUBLE JEOPARDY!

CHINA

Clue	Value	Response
THE INITIAL PHASE OF THIS LARGE BARRIER ALONG THE FRONTIER WAS COMPLETED AROUND 204 B.C.	$200	WHAT IS
ONE OF HER LAST BOOKS WAS 1972's "CHINA PAST AND PRESENT"	$400	WHO IS
THE CEDING OF HONG KONG TO GREAT BRITAIN WAS ONE RESULT OF 2 WARS NAMED FOR THIS SUBSTANCE	$600	WHAT IS
ITS PRINCIPAL TRIBUTARIES INCLUDE THE JIALING, THE MIN & THE YALONG	$800	WHAT IS
THIS MAN LED THE 1911 REVOLUTIONARY MOVEMENT DEDICATED TO ESTABLISHING DEMOCRACY IN CHINA	$1000	WHO IS

DOUBLE JEOPARDY!

CHINA

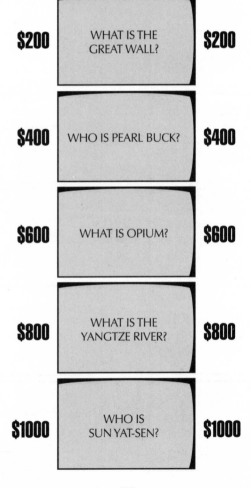

$200 WHAT IS THE GREAT WALL? **$200**

$400 WHO IS PEARL BUCK? **$400**

$600 WHAT IS OPIUM? **$600**

$800 WHAT IS THE YANGTZE RIVER? **$800**

$1000 WHO IS SUN YAT-SEN? **$1000**

DOUBLE JEOPARDY!

WHAT A "GREAT" MOVIE!

THIS DICKENS NOVEL HAS BEEN FILMED SEVERAL TIMES, MOST RECENTLY IN 1998	**$200**	WHAT IS
JOHN BARRYMORE SPOOFED HIMSELF IN THIS 1940 MOVIE WHOSE TITLE REFLECTED HIS NICKNAME	**$400**	WHAT IS
ROBERT DUVALL IS AN AUTHORITARIAN MARINE AT WAR WITH HIS FAMILY IN THIS FILM BASED ON PAT CONROY'S NOVEL	**$600**	WHAT IS
SIMON WARD PLAYED JAMES HERRIOT AS A YOUNG APPRENTICE TO AN ECCENTRIC VETERINARIAN IN THIS 1974 FILM	**$800**	WHAT IS
CHARLIE CHAPLIN PLAYED ON THE PHYSICAL RESEMBLANCE OF HITLER & THE LITTLE TRAMP IN THIS 1940 SATIRE	**$1000**	WHAT IS

DOUBLE JEOPARDY!

WHAT A "GREAT" MOVIE!

$200	WHAT IS "GREAT EXPECTATIONS"?	**$200**
$400	WHAT IS "THE GREAT PROFILE"?	**$400**
$600	WHAT IS "THE GREAT SANTINI"?	**$600**
$800	WHAT IS "ALL CREATURES GREAT AND SMALL"?	**$800**
$1000	WHAT IS "THE GREAT DICTATOR"?	**$1000**

DOUBLE JEOPARDY!

FOREVER

Clue	Value	Response
THE BANGLES HIT ABOUT AN "ETERNAL" ONE LIT UP THE NO. 1 SPOT ON THE CHARTS IN 1989	**$200**	WHAT IS
FICTIONAL CANDY MAKER WHO CREATED THE EVERLASTING GOBSTOPPER	**$400**	WHO IS
IT'S A THEORETICAL DEVICE THAT ONCE RUNNING GOES FOREVER WITHOUT ANY ADDITIONAL INPUTS OF ENERGY	**$600**	WHAT IS
ZEUS CONDEMNED HIM TO THE HELLISH REGION OF TARTARUS & AN ETERNITY OF PUSHING A ROCK UP A HILL	**$800**	WHO IS
MICHAEL ENDE'S STORY OF A BOY WHO ENTERS A FANTASY WORLD WHEN HE READS A BOOK ABOUT IT	**$1000**	WHAT IS

225

DOUBLE JEOPARDY!

FOREVER

$200	WHAT IS A(N ETERNAL) FLAME?	**$200**
$400	WHO IS WILLY WONKA?	**$400**
$600	WHAT IS A PERPETUAL MOTION MACHINE?	**$600**
$800	WHO IS SISYPHUS?	**$800**
$1000	WHAT IS "THE NEVERENDING STORY"?	**$1000**

DOUBLE JEOPARDY!

BOOKS & AUTHORS

IN 1998 HE BROUGHT BACK EX-NAVY SEAL & FORMER CIA AGENT JOHN CLARK IN THE TECHNO-THRILLER "RAINBOW SIX"	**$200**	WHO IS
THIS JOHN GRISHAM BESTSELLER ABOUT CORRUPTION IN THE INSURANCE BUSINESS WAS TURNED INTO A 1997 FILM	**$400**	WHAT IS
HIS 1950 CLASSIC "I, ROBOT" CONTAINS 9 RELATED STORIES ABOUT (WHAT ELSE?) ROBOTS	**$600**	WHO IS
SHE WROTE ABOUT HER FATHER & "WOMEN OF COURAGE" AS WELL AS OF MURDER "IN GEORGETOWN"	**$800**	WHO IS
THIS CAMUS NOVEL IS KNOWN IN FRENCH AS "LA PESTE"	**$1000**	WHAT IS

DOUBLE JEOPARDY!

BOOKS & AUTHORS

$200	WHO IS TOM CLANCY?	**$200**
$400	WHAT IS "THE RAINMAKER"?	**$400**
$600	WHO IS ISAAC ASIMOV?	**$600**
$800	WHO IS MARGARET TRUMAN (DANIEL)?	**$800**
$1000	WHAT IS "THE PLAGUE"?	**$1000**

DOUBLE JEOPARDY!

CHARLEMAGNE

Clue	Value	Response
CHARLEMAGNE'S FIRST TITLE WAS KING OF THESE PEOPLE; HE NEVER WAS KING OF THE BEANS	$200	WHO ARE
IN SUBDUING THE SAXONS, CHARLEMAGNE EXECUTED THOSE WHO REFUSED THIS CHRISTIAN RITE	$400	WHAT IS
WHILE SERVING IN THIS POST IN 799 LEO III WAS ATTACKED IN ROME & TOOK REFUGE IN CHARLEMAGNE'S COURT	$600	WHAT IS
A SCHOLARLY KING, CHARLEMAGNE ENJOYED HAVING THIS SAINT'S "CITY OF GOD" READ TO HIM	$800	WHO IS
CHARLEMAGNE LOST HIS REAR GUARD, LED BY THIS LEGENDARY NEPHEW ALSO CALLED ORLANDO, AT RONCESVALLES	$1000	WHO IS

DOUBLE JEOPARDY!

CHARLEMAGNE

$200	WHO ARE THE FRANKS?	**$200**
$400	WHAT IS BAPTISM?	**$400**
$600	WHAT IS POPE?	**$600**
$800	WHO IS ST. AUGUSTINE?	**$800**
$1000	WHO IS ROLAND?	**$1000**

DOUBLE JEOPARDY!

FASHION STATEMENTS

IF YOU'RE DISCOVERED IN AN EMBARRASSING SITUATION, YOU'RE SAID TO BE CAUGHT "WITH" THESE "DOWN"	**$200**	WHAT ARE
WHEN YOU CONCEAL SOMETHING, YOU "DRAW" THIS BRIDAL ACCESSORY "OVER IT"	**$400**	WHAT IS
A PHRASE THAT MEANS OUTDATED, OR A DERBY YOU HAVEN'T WORN FOR DECADES	**$600**	WHAT IS
IT'S BELIEVED NAPOLEON ORIGINATED THE PHRASE ABOUT "AN IRON HAND IN" ONE OF THESE	**$800**	WHAT IS
AS GARIBALDI'S FOLLOWERS WERE KNOWN AS REDSHIRTS, MUSSOLINI'S DEVOTEES WERE CALLED THESE	**$1000**	WHAT ARE

DOUBLE JEOPARDY!

FASHION STATEMENTS

$200	WHAT ARE YOUR PANTS?	**$200**
$400	WHAT IS A VEIL?	**$400**
$600	WHAT IS OLD HAT?	**$600**
$800	WHAT IS "A VELVET GLOVE"?	**$800**
$1000	WHAT ARE BLACKSHIRTS?	**$1000**

FINAL JEOPARDY!

CONDUCTORS

"REACHING FOR THE NOTE"
WAS THE SUBTITLE OF A
1998 FILM ABOUT THIS
AMERICAN MUSIC LEGEND
WHO DIED IN 1990

WHO IS

FINAL JEOPARDY!

CONDUCTORS

WHO IS
LEONARD BERNSTEIN?

JEOPARDY!

COUNTY SEATS

Clue	Value	Response
HILO, I LOVE YOU, YOU'RE THE SEAT OF THIS COUNTY THAT'S ALSO A "BIG ISLAND"	$100	WHAT IS
PARIS (POPULATION 8,730) IS THE SEAT OF BOURBON COUNTY IN THIS STATE	$200	WHAT IS
THIS IOWA CITY, THE SEAT OF BLACK HAWK COUNTRY, HAS A NAME WELLINGTON WOULD REMEMBER	$300	WHAT IS
QUINCY, ILLINOIS IS THE SEAT OF A COUNTY WITH THIS PRESIDENTIAL NAME	$400	WHAT IS
AS I WALKED OUT IN THE STREETS OF THIS CITY, I WAS IN THE SEAT OF WEBB COUNTY, TEXAS	$500	WHAT IS

JEOPARDY!

COUNTY SEATS

$100	WHAT IS HAWAII?	**$100**
$200	WHAT IS KENTUCKY?	**$200**
$300	WHAT IS WATERLOO?	**$300**
$400	WHAT IS ADAMS?	**$400**
$500	WHAT IS LAREDO?	**$500**

JEOPARDY!

WEAPONS

A PERSON WHOSE RECKLESS BEHAVIOR PUTS OTHERS IN DANGER IS A "LOOSE" ONE OF THESE	**$100**	WHAT IS
THE WORD HOWITZER MAY GO BACK TO THE CZECH WORD HOUF-NICE, THIS WEAPON CARRIED BY DENNIS THE MENACE	**$200**	WHAT IS
BELGIAN NOEL GODIN MASTERMINDED A FEBRUARY 1998 HIT ON BILL GATES WITH ONE OF THESE	**$300**	WHAT IS
ANTHONY HOPKINS SAID HE GOT SO GOOD WITH THIS WEAPON DOING "ZORRO" HE COULD SNAP A TWIG OFF A TREE WITH IT	**$400**	WHAT IS
A KEY ISSUE OF THE 1998 ATTORNEY GENERAL'S RACE IN CALIFORNIA WAS THE BAN ON THESE SEMI-AUTOMATIC WEAPONS	**$500**	WHAT ARE

237

JEOPARDY!

WEAPONS

$100 — WHAT IS A CANNON? — $100

$200 — WHAT IS A SLINGSHOT? — $200

$300 — WHAT IS A (CREAM) PIE? — $300

$400 — WHAT IS A WHIP? — $400

$500 — WHAT ARE ASSAULT RIFLES? — $500

238

JEOPARDY!

LEGENDS OF SPORTS

THIS FORMER 49ers QB WHO HOLDS MANY SUPER BOWL RECORDS ALMOST PLAYED COLLEGE BASKETBALL INSTEAD OF FOOTBALL	**$100**	WHO IS
A BRANTFORD, ONTARIO NATIVE, THIS "GREAT ONE" REWROTE THE NHL RECORD BOOKS	**$200**	WHO IS
SADLY, THIS UNDEFEATED BOXING LEGEND FROM BROCK-TON, MASSACHUSETTS DIED IN A PLANE CRASH IN 1969	**$300**	WHO IS
THIS 1932 OLYMPIC GOLD MEDAL WINNER IS OFTEN CALLED THE GREATEST FEMALE ATHLETE OF ALL TIME	**$400**	WHO IS
HIS LIFETIME BATTING AVERAGE WAS .366— NOT .367, NO MATTER WHAT YOU'VE READ	**$500**	WHO IS

JEOPARDY!

LEGENDS OF SPORTS

$100	WHO IS JOE MONTANA?	**$100**
$200	WHO IS WAYNE GRETZKY?	**$200**
$300	WHO IS ROCKY MARCIANO?	**$300**
$400	WHO IS MILDRED "BABE" DIDRIKSON (ZAHARIAS)?	**$400**
$500	WHO IS TY COBB?	**$500**

JEOPARDY!

BRITISH PRIME MINISTERS

HIS LAST TERM AS PRIME MINISTER ENDED IN 1955, THE YEAR HE TURNED 81	**$100**	WHO IS
HE HAD A TOUGH ACT TO FOLLOW: MARGARET THATCHER	**$200**	WHO IS
PM FROM 1937 TO 1940, HE'S LARGELY REMEMBERED AS A REALLY BAD JUDGE OF CHARACTER	**$300**	WHO IS
THE ELDER WAS PM FROM 1766 TO 1768; THE YOUNGER, FROM 1783 TO 1801 & FROM 1804 TO 1806	**$400**	WHO IS
"MERCIFUL" FIRST NAME OF POSTWAR PM ATTLEE	**$500**	WHAT IS

JEOPARDY!

BRITISH PRIME MINISTERS

$100 WHO IS WINSTON CHURCHILL? **$100**

$200 WHO IS JOHN MAJOR? **$200**

$300 WHO IS NEVILLE CHAMBERLAIN? **$300**

$400 WHO IS WILLIAM PITT? **$400**

$500 WHAT IS CLEMENT? **$500**

JEOPARDY!

I WAS FIRST

HELLO OUT THERE ... IN 1969 THIS PRESIDENT PLACED THE FIRST TELEPHONE CALL TO THE MOON	**$100**	WHO IS
IN 1930 ELLEN CHURCH WAS FLYING HIGH AS THE FIRST WOMAN TO SERVE THE AIRLINES IN THIS CAPACITY	**$200**	WHAT IS
TIRED OF CARRYING 2 PAIRS OF GLASSES AROUND, BENJAMIN FRANKLIN INVENTED THESE	**$300**	WHAT ARE
MICKEY MOUSE FOUND HIS VOICE IN THIS 1928 CARTOON, THE FIRST TO FEATURE SYNCHRONIZED SOUND	**$400**	WHAT IS
A MEMBER OF CONGRESS FROM 1940 TO 1973, THIS DOWN EASTER WAS THE FIRST WOMAN TO SERVE IN THE HOUSE & SENATE	**$500**	WHO IS

JEOPARDY!

I WAS FIRST

$100	WHO IS RICHARD NIXON?	**$100**
$200	WHAT IS FLIGHT ATTENDANT?	**$200**
$300	WHAT ARE BIFOCALS?	**$300**
$400	WHAT IS "STEAMBOAT WILLIE"?	**$400**
$500	WHO IS MARGARET CHASE SMITH?	**$500**

JEOPARDY!

"SO" WHAT?

LEONTYNE PRICE, BEVERLY SILLS, OR THEIR SINGING VOICE	**$100**	WHAT IS
IT'S A SPEECH GIVEN BY A CHARACTER IN A PLAY WHILE ALONE— "TO BE OR NOT TO BE", FOR EXAMPLE	**$200**	WHAT IS
ELEGANT & REFINED, LIKE DUKE ELLINGTON'S "LADY"	**$300**	WHAT IS
IT'S A GLASSED-IN ROOM OR GALLERY WHERE YOU CAN CATCH SOME RAYS	**$400**	WHAT IS
IN 1992 SUPERMODEL IMAN RETURNED TO THIS COUNTRY OF HER BIRTH FOR A DOCUMENTARY ON THE FAMINE THERE	**$500**	WHAT IS

JEOPARDY!

"SO" WHAT?

$100	WHAT IS SOPRANO?	$100
$200	WHAT IS A SOLILOQUY?	$200
$300	WHAT IS SOPHISTICATED?	$300
$400	WHAT IS A SOLARIUM?	$400
$500	WHAT IS SOMALIA?	$500

DOUBLE JEOPARDY!

OPERA

Clue	Value	Response
GUILTY OVER HER AFFAIR WITH BORIS, THE HEROINE OF "KATYA KABANOVA" DROWNS HERSELF IN THIS RUSSIAN RIVER	**$200**	WHAT IS
FERENC ERKEL'S 1844 WORK "HUNYADY LASZLO" IS ONE OF THIS COUNTRY'S MOST FAMOUS OPERAS	**$400**	WHAT IS
MINNIE RUNS A SALOON IN A CALIFORNIA MINING CAMP IN THIS ITALIAN COMPOSER'S OPERA "THE GIRL OF THE GOLDEN WEST"	**$600**	WHO IS
"DIE HARMONIE DER WELT" EXPLORES THE LIFE OF THIS ASTRONOMER & HIS MUSICAL THEORIES OF PLANETARY MOTION	**$800**	WHO IS
THE HEROINE OF THIS CZECH COMPOSER'S 1881 OPERA "LIBUSE" IS THE QUEEN OF BOHEMIA	**$1000**	WHO IS

DOUBLE JEOPARDY!

OPERA

$200	WHAT IS THE VOLGA?
$400	WHAT IS HUNGARY?
$600	WHO IS GIACOMO PUCCINI?
$800	WHO IS JOHANNES KEPLER?
$1000	WHO IS BEDRICH SMETANA?

DOUBLE JEOPARDY!

1980s FADS

TORN SWEATSHIRTS & LEGWARMERS WERE ALL THE RAGE AFTER THIS 1983 JENNIFER BEALS MOVIE	**$200**	WHAT IS
SENSITIVE MEN OF THE '70s WERE OUT; "REAL MEN" DIDN'T EAT THIS	**$400**	WHAT IS
ANDROGYNY WAS EXEMPLIFIED BY EURYTHMICS' ANNIE LENNOX, & BY THIS LEAD SINGER OF THE CULTURE CLUB	**$600**	WHO IS
BASED ON XAVIER ROBERTS' SCULPTURES, THESE DOLLS WERE A POPULAR ITEM FOR ADOPTION IN 1983	**$800**	WHAT ARE
GREED WAS GOOD: TRUMP TAUGHT "THE ART OF THE DEAL", & SHE SAID, "ONLY THE LITTLE PEOPLE PAY TAXES"	**$1000**	WHO IS

DOUBLE JEOPARDY!

1980s FADS

$200	WHAT IS "FLASHDANCE"?	**$200**
$400	WHAT IS QUICHE?	**$400**
$600	WHO IS BOY GEORGE?	**$600**
$800	WHAT ARE CABBAGE PATCH KIDS?	**$800**
$1000	WHO IS LEONA HELMSLEY?	**$1000**

DOUBLE JEOPARDY!

INVENTORS

THIS PHONOGRAPH INVENTOR'S SON CHARLES SERVED AS GOVERNOR OF NEW JERSEY FROM 1941 TO 1944	**$200**	WHO IS
AROUND 1045 PI SHENG CAME UP WITH THIS MOVABLE INVENTION, LATER USED BY GUTENBERG	**$400**	WHAT IS
IN 1857 THIS TELEGRAPH INVENTOR SERVED AS THE ELECTRICIAN ON CYRUS FIELD'S FIRST TRANSATLANTIC CABLE ATTEMPT	**$600**	WHO IS
IN THE 1850s HE PATENTED THE FOOT TREADLE FOR HIS SEWING MACHINE	**$800**	WHO IS
IN 1854 HORACE SMITH & THIS PARTNER PATENTED THE REPEATING RIFLE & REVOLVER	**$1000**	WHO IS

DOUBLE JEOPARDY!

INVENTORS

$200	WHO IS THOMAS A. EDISON?	**$200**
$400	WHAT IS MOVABLE TYPE?	**$400**
$600	WHO IS SAMUEL F.B. MORSE?	**$600**
$800	WHO IS ISAAC M. SINGER?	**$800**
$1000	WHO IS DANIEL B. WESSON?	**$1000**

DOUBLE JEOPARDY!

A CINEMATIC TRIP TO VEGAS

NICOLAS CAGE DRIVES TO THE DESERT TO DRINK HIMSELF TO DEATH & MEETS AN ANGELIC HOOKER IN THIS 1995 DRAMA	**$200**	WHAT IS
FELONS SKYJACK A PLANE WITH NICOLAS CAGE (WHO ELSE?) ON BOARD & CRASH-LAND ON THE VEGAS STRIP IN THIS 1997 THRILLER	**$400**	WHAT IS
NICOLAS CAGE (OF COURSE) SKYDIVES INTO VEGAS WITH A TROOP OF ELVIS IMPERSONATORS IN THIS 1992 COMEDY	**$600**	WHAT IS
1996 FILM IN WHICH L.A. HIPSTERS VINCE VAUGHN & JON FAVREAU TAKE A ROAD TRIP TO "VEGAS, BABY, VEGAS!"	**$800**	WHAT IS
FRANK SINATRA LEADS 10 OTHER MEN IN AN ATTEMPT TO ROB 5 VEGAS CASINOS IN THIS 1960 CLASSIC	**$1000**	WHAT IS

DOUBLE JEOPARDY!

A CINEMATIC TRIP TO VEGAS

$200 — WHAT IS "LEAVING LAS VEGAS"? — $200

$400 — WHAT IS "CON AIR"? — $400

$600 — WHAT IS "HONEYMOON IN VEGAS"? — $600

$800 — WHAT IS "SWINGERS"? — $800

$1000 — WHAT IS "OCEAN'S ELEVEN"? — $1000

DOUBLE JEOPARDY!

ANCIENT HISTORY

THIS COUNTRY'S SHANG DYNASTY AROSE IN THE 1700s B.C. ALONG THE YELLOW RIVER	**$200**	WHAT IS
IN 439 A.D. THIS NORTH AFRICAN CITY-STATE WAS CONQUERED BY THE VANDALS UNDER GENSERIC	**$400**	WHAT IS
IN 303 A.D. DIOCLETIAN FORBADE CHRISTIAN WORSHIP; THIS MAN, HIS "GREAT" SUCCESSOR, REVOKED THE EDICT 10 YEARS LATER	**$600**	WHO IS
SCULPTURE BY SCOPAS DECORATED THIS TOMB AT HALICARNASSUS, ONE OF THE 7 ANCIENT WONDERS	**$800**	WHAT IS
WHEN HE DIED AROUND 347 B.C., HIS NEPHEW SPEUSIPPUS TOOK OVER LEADERSHIP OF THE ACADEMY	**$1000**	WHO IS

DOUBLE JEOPARDY!

ANCIENT HISTORY

$200	WHAT IS CHINA?	**$200**
$400	WHAT IS CARTHAGE?	**$400**
$600	WHO IS CONSTANTINE (I OR THE GREAT)?	**$600**
$800	WHAT IS THE MAUSOLEUM?	**$800**
$1000	WHO IS PLATO?	**$1000**

DOUBLE JEOPARDY!

3-LETTER WORDS

Clue	Value	Response
IT'S ONE LAYER OF TOILET PAPER OR WOOD	$200	WHAT IS
A YOUNG FISH, A WAY TO COOK IT, OR A "SMALL" (UNIMPORTANT) PERSON	$400	WHAT IS
AN EYE IRRITATION, OR A PIGPEN	$600	WHAT IS
A LARGE COFFEE CONTAINER, OR A LARGE VASE TO STASH ONE'S ASHES	$800	WHAT IS
IT EQUALS 1/1000th OF AN INCH	$1000	WHAT IS

DOUBLE JEOPARDY!

3-LETTER WORDS

$200   WHAT IS PLY? $200

$400   WHAT IS FRY? $400

$600   WHAT IS STY? $600

$800   WHAT IS URN? $800

$1000   WHAT IS MIL? $1000

FINAL JEOPARDY!

FAMOUS WOMEN

DURING WWI THIS
AMERICAN SHOWED OFF
HER TALENTS IN A PLAY
CALLED "THE WESTERN GIRL"

WHO IS

FINAL JEOPARDY!

FAMOUS WOMEN

WHO IS ANNIE OAKLEY?

JEOPARDY!

HISTORY

Clue	Value	Response
1903's TREATY OF PETROPOLIS "ERASED" A SOUTH AMERICAN DISPUTE OVER AN AREA RICH IN THIS PLANT RESOURCE	$100	WHAT IS
IN 1931 THE INVADING JAPANESE MADE THIS CHINESE AREA A PUPPET STATE CALLED MANCHUKUO	$200	WHAT IS
THE LIMITED IRISH AUTONOMY PROPOSED BY ISAAC BUTT AROUND 1870 WAS CALLED THIS TYPE OF "RULE"	$300	WHAT IS
BRUGGE IN FLEMISH, THIS BELGIAN CITY'S TRADE DECLINED WITH THE SILTING OF THE ZWYN RIVER IN THE 1400s	$400	WHAT IS
IN 897 POPE STEPHEN VI HAD HIS PREDECESSOR FORMOSUS EXHUMED, PUT ON TRIAL & THROWN INTO THIS RIVER	$500	WHAT IS

JEOPARDY!

HISTORY

$100 WHAT IS RUBBER? **$100**

$200 WHAT IS MANCHURIA? **$200**

$300 WHAT IS HOME RULE? **$300**

$400 WHAT IS BRUGES? **$400**

$500 WHAT IS THE TIBER? **$500**

262

JEOPARDY!

ANIMAL BEHAVIOR

THIS DOMESTIC ANIMAL'S CIRCLING MOVEMENT BEFORE LYING DOWN GOES BACK TO A GRASS-FLATTENING BEHAVIOR	**$100**	WHAT IS
SALMON DEPEND MAINLY ON THIS SENSE TO FIND THEIR NATIVE RIVERS	**$200**	WHAT IS
SOME FROGS RETRACT THEIR EYES TO HELP THEM DO THIS AFTER CATCHING A FLY	**$300**	WHAT IS
THE EMPEROR VARIETY OF THIS BIRD CAN STAY UNDERWATER FOR 18 MINUTES	**$400**	WHAT IS
DOMINANCE WAS FIRST DISCOVERED IN FLOCKS OF CHICKENS, HENCE THIS COMMON HIERARCHICAL PHRASE	**$500**	WHAT IS

JEOPARDY!

ANIMAL BEHAVIOR

$100	WHAT IS THE DOG?	**$100**
$200	WHAT IS SMELL?	**$200**
$300	WHAT IS SWALLOW?	**$300**
$400	WHAT IS THE PENGUIN?	**$400**
$500	WHAT IS PECK(ING) ORDER?	**$500**

JEOPARDY!

FILM FOLK

Clue	Value	Response
JOHN SINGLETON DIRECTED SAMUEL L. JACKSON AS THIS DETECTIVE, NEPHEW OF THE SEX MACHINE OF THE SAME NAME	$100	WHO IS
WHEN "GOD CREATED" THIS FRENCH FILM SEX SYMBOL OF THE '50s & '60s, SHE WAS CAMILLE JAVAL	$200	WHO IS
THIS GOATEED MTV STAR PLAYED BARRY IN THE HIT 2000 COMEDY "ROAD TRIP"	$300	WHO IS
HELEN HAYES WON A 1970 OSCAR FOR PLAYING AN IMPISH STOWAWAY IN THIS FILM THAT WAS FOLLOWED BY 3 SEQUELS	$400	WHAT IS
SCOTT WILSON & ROBERT BLAKE PORTRAYED THE DOOMED KILLERS IN THIS SHOCKING BLACK & WHITE CLASSIC	$500	WHAT IS

JEOPARDY!

FILM FOLK

$100	WHO IS JOHN SHAFT?	$100
$200	WHO IS BRIGITTE BARDOT?	$200
$300	WHO IS TOM GREEN?	$300
$400	WHAT IS "AIRPORT"?	$400
$500	WHAT IS "IN COLD BLOOD"?	$500

JEOPARDY!

LITERARY SAN FRANCISCO

"DO NOT GO GENTLE INTO" VESUVIO, A FAVORITE WATERING HOLE OF THE BEAT GENERATION & OF THIS WELSH POET	**$100**	WHO IS
JOHN'S GRILL ON ELLIS STREET IS FAMOUS BECAUSE SAM SPADE DINED THERE IN THIS NOVEL	**$200**	WHAT IS
WHEN YOU VISIT THE CITY LIGHTS BOOK-STORE, LOOK FOR THE NEARBY STREET NAMED FOR THIS "ON THE ROAD" AUTHOR	**$300**	WHO IS
OSCAR WILDE & THIS "GUNGA DIN" AUTHOR BOTH STAYED IN THE PALACE HOTEL—PRESUMABLY NOT TOGETHER	**$400**	WHO IS
HE DETAILED THE HIGH LIFE IN HAIGHT-ASHBURY IN HIS '60s OPUS "THE ELECTRIC KOOL-AID ACID TEST"	**$500**	WHO IS

267

JEOPARDY!

LITERARY SAN FRANCISCO

$100	WHO IS DYLAN THOMAS?	**$100**
$200	WHAT IS "THE MALTESE FALCON"?	**$200**
$300	WHO IS JACK KEROUAC?	**$300**
$400	WHO IS RUDYARD KIPLING?	**$400**
$500	WHO IS TOM WOLFE?	**$500**

JEOPARDY!

HOLIDAYS & OBSERVANCES

HOLIDAY ASSOCIATED WITH THE "WEARING OF THE GREEN"	**$100**	WHAT IS
IT HONORS 2 GREAT AMERICANS, BORN IN FEBRUARY 1732 & FEBRUARY 1809	**$200**	WHAT IS
THIS HOLIDAY IS CELEBRATED ON WHAT WAS ONCE THE LAST DAY OF THE CELTIC YEAR	**$300**	WHAT IS
ALTHOUGH FIRST OBSERVED IN 1909, IT WASN'T UNTIL 1972 THAT THE THIRD SUN-DAY IN JUNE OFFICIALLY BECAME THIS HOLIDAY	**$400**	WHAT IS
ID AL-FITR IS A DAY OF FEASTING THAT ENDS THE FAST AT THE END OF THIS ISLAMIC HOLY MONTH	**$500**	WHAT IS

JEOPARDY!

HOLIDAYS & OBSERVANCES

$100	WHAT IS ST. PATRICK'S DAY?	**$100**
$200	WHAT IS PRESIDENTS DAY?	**$200**
$300	WHAT IS HALLOWEEN?	**$300**
$400	WHAT IS FATHER'S DAY?	**$400**
$500	WHAT IS RAMADAN?	**$500**

JEOPARDY!

"WHOLE"SOME

IF FREDDY, WILBUR OR BABE INDULGED HIMSELF COMPLETELY, HE'D "GO" THIS	$100	WHAT IS
A COMPLETELY FICTITIOUS TALE IS "MADE OUT OF" THIS	$200	WHAT IS
IN A JOKING W.C. FIELDS EPITAPH, THESE 3 WORDS PRECEDE "I'D RATHER BE IN PHILADELPHIA"	$300	WHAT ARE
SHEBEEN, A WORD FOR AN IRISH TAVERN, MAY BE THE ORIGIN OF THIS EXPRESSION	$400	WHAT IS
COMPLETES THE FAMOUS ALKA-SELTZER AD LINE, "I CAN'T BELIEVE . . ."	$500	WHAT IS

JEOPARDY!

"WHOLE"SOME

$100	WHAT IS WHOLE HOG?	$100
$200	WHAT IS WHOLE CLOTH?	$200
$300	WHAT ARE "ON THE WHOLE"?	$300
$400	WHAT IS THE WHOLE SHEBANG?	$400
$500	WHAT IS "I ATE THE WHOLE THING"?	$500

DOUBLE JEOPARDY!

THE MIDWEST

Clue	Value	Response
WHEN ONE SAYS "TWIN CITIES", IT'S USUALLY THIS MINNESOTA PAIR	$200	WHAT ARE
THIS CITY IS HOME TO THE NATIONAL RAILROAD MUSEUM & THE FIRST SUPER BOWL CHAMP	$400	WHAT IS
THIS CONTROVERSIAL LABOR LEADER WAS BORN IN 1913 IN BRAZIL—BRAZIL, INDIANA	$600	WHO IS
THE TOWNS OF ROMEO & JULIET IN ILLINOIS BECAME ROMEOVILLE & THIS	$800	WHAT IS
JOSIAH GRINNELL HEEDED THIS ADVICE THAT HORACE GREELEY GAVE HIM & MOVED FROM WASHINGTON, D.C. TO IOWA	$1000	WHAT IS

DOUBLE JEOPARDY!

THE MIDWEST

$200 — WHAT ARE MINNEAPOLIS & ST. PAUL? — **$200**

$400 — WHAT IS GREEN BAY (WISCONSIN)? — **$400**

$600 — WHO IS JIMMY HOFFA? — **$600**

$800 — WHAT IS JOLIET? — **$800**

$1000 — WHAT IS "GO WEST YOUNG MAN (AND GROW UP WITH THE COUNTRY)"? — **$1000**

DOUBLE JEOPARDY!

THE NUDE IN ART

LIKE ANOTHER FAMOUS PAINTER, WILLIAM-ADOLPHE BOUGUEREAU SHOWS HER NUDE ON A SHELL FOR HER "BIRTH"	**$200**	WHO IS
THE SEATED NUDE IN HIS "LES DEMOISELLES D'AVIGNON" SHOWS THE BEGINNINGS OF HIS CUBISM	**$400**	WHO IS
WHEN DURER PAINTED THIS PAIR IN 1507 HE HAD THEM HOLD TREE BRANCHES WHOSE LEAVES BLOCKED OUT CERTAIN PARTS	**$600**	WHO ARE
SHORTLY AFTER HIS "LUNCHEON", THIS IMPRESSIONIST EXHIBITED THE NUDE "OLYMPIA"	**$800**	WHO IS
PEOPLE SAID HIS MALE NUDE "THE AGE OF BRONZE" WAS SO LIFELIKE, HE MUST HAVE MADE CASTS FROM LIVE MODELS	**$1000**	WHO IS

DOUBLE JEOPARDY!

THE NUDE IN ART

$200	WHO IS VENUS?	**$200**
$400	WHO IS PABLO PICASSO?	**$400**
$600	WHO ARE ADAM & EVE?	**$600**
$800	WHO IS EDOUARD MANET?	**$800**
$1000	WHO IS AUGUSTE RODIN?	**$1000**

DOUBLE JEOPARDY!

THE SPORTING LIFE

Clue	Value	Response
THIS BASKETBALL STAR IS THE ONLY MAN PICKED AP's ATHLETE OF THE YEAR 3 YEARS IN A ROW: 1991, 1992 & 1993	$200	WHO IS
ELECTED TO THE HALL OF FAME IN 1999, HE WALKED 2,795 BATTERS BUT STRUCK OUT OVER TWICE AS MANY	$400	WHO IS
THIS SKI EVENT COMES IN REGULAR, GIANT & SUPER GIANT VARIETIES	$600	WHAT IS
IN 1998 A DRUG SCANDAL CAUSED 93 OF 189 RIDERS TO DROP OUT OF THIS EUROPEAN BIKE RACE	$800	WHAT IS
KENYAN MEN TOOK FIRST & SECOND IN THIS RACE APRIL 20, 1998	$1000	WHAT IS

DOUBLE JEOPARDY!

THE SPORTING LIFE

$200	WHO IS MICHAEL JORDAN?	**$200**
$400	WHO IS NOLAN RYAN?	**$400**
$600	WHAT IS THE SLALOM?	**$600**
$800	WHAT IS THE TOUR DE FRANCE?	**$800**
$1000	WHAT IS THE BOSTON MARATHON?	**$1000**

DOUBLE JEOPARDY!

THEORIES

THE THEORY THAT LED TO REAGANOMICS GOT THIS NAME BY OPPOSING THE TRADITIONAL FOCUS ON DEMAND	$200	WHAT IS
DARWIN CALLED HIS BOOK "ON THE ORIGIN OF SPECIES BY MEANS OF NATURAL" THIS	$400	WHAT IS
A 1944 BOOK LAUNCHED THIS FIELD THAT CAN DISSECT ACTIVITIES LIKE POKER & CHECKERS	$600	WHAT IS
OPPOSED TO THE BIG BANG THEORY, SIR FRED HOYLE DEVELOPED THIS THEORY OF A CONSISTENT UNIVERSE	$800	WHAT IS
THORSTEIN VEBLEN COINED "CONSPICUOUS CONSUMPTION" IN "THE THEORY OF" THIS "CLASS"	$1000	WHAT IS

DOUBLE JEOPARDY!

THEORIES

$200 WHAT IS SUPPLY-SIDE ECONOMICS? **$200**

$400 WHAT IS SELECTION? **$400**

$600 WHAT IS GAME THEORY? **$600**

$800 WHAT IS THE STEADY-STATE THEORY? **$800**

$1000 WHAT IS THE LEISURE CLASS? **$1000**

DOUBLE JEOPARDY!

A BIT WORDY

WHAT THE OLD NORSE KNEW AS THORSDAGR, WE CALL THIS TODAY	**$200**	WHAT IS
OF A PERSON, PLACE OR THING, IT'S WHAT THE ROSETTA STONE WAS NAMED FOR	**$400**	WHAT IS
FROM THE GREEK FOR A "RACE DISCOURSE", IT'S THE HISTORY OF A FAMILY	**$600**	WHAT IS
THE WORDS JOURNEY, JOURNAL & DIURNAL ARE ALL BASED ON THIS UNIT OF TIME	**$800**	WHAT IS
ALONE IT MEANS "SILENCE"; ADD "BLE" & IT MEANS TO TALK INDISTINCTLY	**$1000**	WHAT IS

DOUBLE JEOPARDY!

A BIT WORDY

$200   WHAT IS THURSDAY? $200

$400   WHAT IS A PLACE? $400

$600   WHAT IS GENEALOGY? $600

$800   WHAT IS A DAY? $800

$1000   WHAT IS MUM? $1000

DOUBLE JEOPARDY!

HISS-STORY

TRADITION SAYS THAT IN AUGUST 30 B.C. SHE COMMITTED SUICIDE WITH THE BITE OF AN ASP, A SYMBOL OF DIVINE ROYALTY	**$200**	WHO IS
IN GENESIS 3:13 EVE SAID, THIS CREATURE "BEGUILED ME, AND I DID EAT"	**$400**	WHAT IS
PATRIOTIC FLAGS OF THE AMERICAN REVOLUTION DEPICTED A COILED TIMBER RATTLESNAKE & THIS MOTTO	**$600**	WHAT IS
REPTILIAN NICKNAME USED FOR UNION DEMOCRATS WHO OPPOSED LINCOLN'S EFFORTS TO FREE THE SLAVES DURING THE CIVIL WAR	**$800**	WHAT ARE
THIS ANCIENT WINGED STAFF FEATURING 2 INTERTWINED SNAKES IS NOW THE SYMBOL OF THE U.S. ARMY MEDICAL CORPS	**$1000**	WHAT IS

DOUBLE JEOPARDY!

HISS-STORY

$200	WHO IS CLEOPATRA?	**$200**
$400	WHAT IS "THE SERPENT"?	**$400**
$600	WHAT IS "DON'T TREAD ON ME"?	**$600**
$800	WHAT ARE COPPERHEADS?	**$800**
$1000	WHAT IS THE CADUCEUS?	**$1000**

FINAL JEOPARDY!

BUSINESS & INDUSTRY

IN 1903 MORRIS MICHTOM
OF NEW YORK BEGAN
MARKETING THESE WITH
PRESIDENTIAL PERMISSION

WHAT ARE

FINAL JEOPARDY!

BUSINESS & INDUSTRY

WHAT ARE TEDDY BEARS?

JEOPARDY!

TRAVEL & TOURISM

THIS SITE NEAR SALISBURY, ENGLAND HAS HUGE BOULDERS THAT MAY HAVE COME FROM SOUTHERN WALES	$100	WHAT IS
DOW'S LAKE IS PROBABLY THE BEST PLACE TO VIEW THE TULIPS DURING THIS CANADIAN CAPITAL'S MAY TULIP FESTIVAL	$200	WHAT IS
THIS COUNTRY'S TIKAL RUINS WERE ONCE A CEREMONIAL CENTER & THE LARGEST CITY OF THE MAYAN EMPIRE	$300	WHAT IS
THIS OLYMPIC CITY'S FAMOUS SITES INCLUDE A HARBOUR BRIDGE & AN OPERA HOUSE	$400	WHAT IS
THIS STONE PILLAR "OF LUXOR" STANDS 75 FEET HIGH IN THE PLACE DE LA CONCORDE IN PARIS	$500	WHAT IS

JEOPARDY!

TRAVEL & TOURISM

$100 | WHAT IS STONEHENGE? | **$100**

$200 | WHAT IS OTTAWA? | **$200**

$300 | WHAT IS GUATEMALA? | **$300**

$400 | WHAT IS SYDNEY? | **$400**

$500 | WHAT IS THE OBELISK OF LUXOR? | **$500**

JEOPARDY!

SECRETARIES OF COMMERCE

THOUGH SWORN IN 7 MONTHS EARLIER, LEWIS STRAUSS WAS DENIED CONFIRMATION BY THIS BODY IN 1959	**$100**	WHAT IS
LAST NAME OF REAGAN'S COMMERCE SECRETARY MALCOLM, OR HIS SISTER, ETIQUETTE EXPERT LETITIA	**$200**	WHAT IS
IN 1903 GEORGE CORTELYOU MAY HAVE BEEN OVER"WORKED" AS BOTH SECRETARY OF COMMERCE & OF THIS	**$300**	WHAT IS
HE WAS SECRETARY OF COMMERCE FOR MOST OF THE 1920s, BEFORE HE BECAME PRESIDENT	**$400**	WHO IS
THIS FDR ADVISOR DIRECTED THE WPA BEFORE BECOMING COMMERCE SECRETARY IN 1938	**$500**	WHO IS

JEOPARDY!

SECRETARIES OF COMMERCE

$100   WHAT IS THE SENATE?   **$100**

$200   WHAT IS BALDRIGE?   **$200**

$300   WHAT IS LABOR?   **$300**

$400   WHO IS HERBERT HOOVER?   **$400**

$500   WHO IS HARRY HOPKINS?   **$500**

JEOPARDY!

CIVIL WAR SLANG

GRAYBACKS WERE SOUTHERN SOLDIERS; GREENBACKS WERE THIS	$100	WHAT IS
HORNETS WERE THESE, MAYBE FROM A PEPPERBOX PISTOL	$200	WHAT ARE
IF YOU'D DONE A LOT OR HAD A ROUGH EXPERIENCE, YOU'D "BEEN THROUGH" THIS, PERHAPS A COTTON ONE	$300	WHAT IS
THIS TERM FOR "HURRAH!" OR "YEAH!" WAS POPULAR YEARS LATER WITH TEDDY ROOSEVELT	$400	WHAT IS
AN ARKANSAS TOOTHPICK WAS A LARGE ONE OF THESE	$500	WHAT IS

JEOPARDY!

CIVIL WAR SLANG

$100	WHAT IS (U.S.) MONEY?	**$100**
$200	WHAT ARE BULLETS?	**$200**
$300	WHAT IS THE MILL?	**$300**
$400	WHAT IS BULLY?	**$400**
$500	WHAT IS A (BOWIE) KNIFE?	**$500**

JEOPARDY!

SPOUSE IN COMMON

ELLIOT GOULD, JAMES BROLIN	**$100**	WHO IS
HEATHER LOCKLEAR, PAMELA ANDERSON	**$200**	WHO IS
ROGER VADIM, TOM HAYDEN	**$300**	WHO IS
JONNY LEE MILLER, BILLY BOB THORNTON	**$400**	WHO IS
URSULA ANDRESS, LINDA EVANS	**$500**	WHO IS

JEOPARDY!

SPOUSE IN COMMON

$100	WHO IS BARBRA STREISAND?
$200	WHO IS TOMMY LEE?
$300	WHO IS JANE FONDA?
$400	WHO IS ANGELINA JOLIE?
$500	WHO IS JOHN DEREK?

JEOPARDY!

POETS & POETRY

MUCH OF THIS LONGELLOW POEM TAKES PLACE "BY THE SHORES OF GITCHE GUMEE, BY THE SHINING BIG-SEA-WATER"	**$100**	WHAT IS
IN 1630 JOHN MILTON WROTE A SONNET HONORING THIS OTHER FAMOUS SONNETEER	**$200**	WHO IS
VOLTAIRE'S MOCK HEROIC "LA PUCELLE" FEATURES THIS MEDIEVAL WARRIOR MAID	**$300**	WHO IS
ODYSSEUS ELYTIS, A POET FROM THIS COUNTRY, WON THE 1979 NOBEL PRIZE FOR LITERATURE	**$400**	WHAT IS
"CROSSING THE WATER" & "WINTER TREES" ARE 2 POSTHUMOUS COLLECTIONS BY THIS "BELL JAR" AUTHOR	**$500**	WHO IS

JEOPARDY!

POETS & POETRY

$100	WHAT IS "(THE SONG OF) HIAWATHA"?	**$100**
$200	WHO IS WILLIAM SHAKESPEARE?	**$200**
$300	WHO IS JOAN OF ARC?	**$300**
$400	WHAT IS GREECE?	**$400**
$500	WHO IS SYLVIA PLATH?	**$500**

JEOPARDY!

THEY MEANT BUSINESS

HOWARD SCHULTZ MADE THIS CHAIN UBIQUITOUS IN THE U.S. AFTER HAVING AN EPIPHANY OVER ESPRESSO	**$100**	WHAT IS
PRESIDENT HARRY CUNNINGHAM OPENED THIS "K" COMPANY'S FIRST K MART IN MICHIGAN IN 1962	**$200**	WHAT IS
ONE LETTER WAS CHANGED IN THIS TYCOON'S LAST NAME TO GET THE COMPANY NAME REVLON	**$300**	WHO IS
IN THE 1880s MARCUS GOLDMAN WAS JOINED BY THIS SON-IN-LAW & AN INVESTMENT BANKING GIANT WAS BORN	**$400**	WHO IS
CHEMICAL ENGINEER ROBERTO GOIZUETA FLED CUBA & ENDED UP AS CEO OF THIS ATLANTA-BASED COMPANY	**$500**	WHAT IS

JEOPARDY!

THEY MEANT BUSINESS

$100	WHAT IS STARBUCKS?	**$100**
$200	WHAT IS S.S. KRESGE?	**$200**
$300	WHO IS CHARLES REVSON?	**$300**
$400	WHO IS SAMUEL SACHS?	**$400**
$500	WHAT IS COCA-COLA?	**$500**

DOUBLE JEOPARDY!

SCIENCE

Clue	Value	Response
PILTDOWN MAN, A HOAX PLAYED ON SCIENTISTS, HAD A HUMAN SKULL & THE JAW OF THIS REDDISH APE	**$200**	WHAT IS
A WHOLE LOT OF SHAKIN' GOES ON IN THIS SCIENCE THAT DEALS ALMOST EXCLUSIVELY WITH EARTHQUAKES	**$400**	WHAT IS
MASS NUMBER IS DEFINED AS THE NUMBER OF NEUTRONS & THESE PARTICLES IN AN ATOM'S NUCLEUS	**$600**	WHAT ARE
FROM THE LATIN FOR "SMOKE HOLE", IT'S A VENT IN A VOLCANIC AREA FROM WHICH SMOKE & GASES ESCAPE	**$800**	WHAT IS
IN CONTRAST TO THE HYDROSPHERE, IT'S THE TERM FOR THE ROCKY PART OF THE EARTH, OR ITS CRUST	**$1000**	WHAT IS

DOUBLE JEOPARDY!

SCIENCE

$200	WHAT IS AN ORANGUTAN?	**$200**
$400	WHAT IS SEISMOLOGY?	**$400**
$600	WHAT ARE PROTONS?	**$600**
$800	WHAT IS A FUMAROLE?	**$800**
$1000	WHAT IS LITHOSPHERE?	**$1000**

DOUBLE JEOPARDY!

JUST DESSERTS

THIS BRAND OF GELATIN FIRST JIGGLED IN 4 FLAVORS: STRAWBERRY, LEMON, ORANGE & RASPBERRY	**$200**	WHAT IS
DESPITE ITS NAME, SARA LEE'S "ALL BUTTER" ONE IS ONLY 10¾ OUNCES	**$400**	WHAT IS
A HAPPY BAKING ACCIDENT LED TO THE INVENTION OF THIS SEMISOFT CANDY THAT'S OFTEN CHOCOLATE	**$600**	WHAT IS
ONE VARIATION OF THIS COOKIE IS THE DOUBLE STUF, WITH TWICE THE CREME FILLING OF THE ORIGINAL	**$800**	WHAT IS
SEA CAPTAIN HANSON GREGORY & THE PENNSYLVANIA DUTCH ARE BOTH CREDITED WITH PUTTING THE HOLE IN THIS TREAT	**$1000**	WHAT IS

DOUBLE JEOPARDY!

JUST DESSERTS

$200	WHAT IS JELL-O?	**$200**
$400	WHAT IS A POUND CAKE?	**$400**
$600	WHAT IS FUDGE?	**$600**
$800	WHAT IS AN OREO?	**$800**
$1000	WHAT IS A DOUGHNUT (OR DONUT)?	**$1000**

DOUBLE JEOPARDY!

FILMS OF THE '50s

Clue	Value	Response
THIS FILM SET IN THE BRONX FEATURED ANGIE & CLARA AS WELL AS THE ERNEST BORGNINE TITLE CHARACTER	$200	WHAT IS
IN 1959 SANDRA DEE HIT THE BEACH AS THIS TITLE GIRL	$400	WHO IS
COMPLETES THE TITLE OF A FRANK SINATRA DRUG FILM, "THE MAN WITH ..."	$600	WHAT IS
COMPLETES THE TITLE OF A JIMMY STEWART ESPIONAGE FILM, "THE MAN WHO ..."	$800	WHAT IS
COMPLETES THE TITLE OF A GREGORY PECK CORPORATE FILM, "THE MAN IN ..."	$1000	WHAT IS

DOUBLE JEOPARDY!

FILMS OF THE '50s

$200	WHAT IS "MARTY"?	**$200**
$400	WHO IS GIDGET?	**$400**
$600	WHAT IS "THE GOLDEN ARM"?	**$600**
$800	WHAT IS "KNEW TOO MUCH"?	**$800**
$1000	WHAT IS "THE GRAY FLANNEL SUIT"?	**$1000**

DOUBLE JEOPARDY!

WORLD CAPITALS

DURING THE MIDDLE AGES, THIS CAPITAL WAS MOSTLY CONFINED TO STADSHOLMEN & RIDDARHOLMEN ISLANDS	**$200**	WHAT IS
ALEXANDER NEVSKY CATHEDRAL IN THE CENTER OF THIS BULGARIAN CITY CELEBRATES ITS LIBERATION FROM THE TURKS	**$400**	WHAT IS
IN THIS CAPITAL, YOU CAN WATCH THE SUN TURN THE TAGUS' ESTUARY INTO MAR DE PALHA, THE SEA OF STRAW	**$600**	WHAT IS
DIPLOMATS LIVE IN THE CHANAKYAPURI SECTION OF THIS CAPITAL DESIGNED BY EDWIN LUTYENS & HERBERT BAKER	**$800**	WHAT IS
FROM 1936 TO 1961 THIS CARIBBEAN CAPITAL WAS KNOWN AS CIUDAD TRUJILLO IN HONOR OF DICTATOR RAFAEL TRUJILLO	**$1000**	WHAT IS

DOUBLE JEOPARDY!

WORLD CAPITALS

$200	WHAT IS STOCKHOLM?	**$200**
$400	WHAT IS SOFIA?	**$400**
$600	WHAT IS LISBON?	**$600**
$800	WHAT IS NEW DELHI?	**$800**
$1000	WHAT IS SANTO DOMINGO?	**$1000**

DOUBLE JEOPARDY!

AMERICAN REVOLUTIONARIES

2 YEARS BEFORE TURNING TRAITOR, HE RALLIED THE AMERICANS TO VICTORY AT THE SECOND BATTLE OF SARATOGA	**$200**	WHO IS
IN SPEAKING AGAINST THE STAMP ACT IN MAY 1765, HE SAID, "IF THIS BE TREASON, MAKE THE MOST OF IT"	**$400**	WHO IS
IN 1781 HE WAS GIVEN COMMAND OF THE NAVY'S LARGEST SHIP, AMERICA, BUT THE SHIP WAS TURNED OVER TO FRANCE	**$600**	WHO IS
IN "COMMON SENSE", HE WROTE, "THERE IS SOMETHING EXCEED-INGLY RIDICULOUS IN THE COMPOSITION OF MONARCHY"	**$800**	WHO IS
BORN TO A PROS-PEROUS BOSTON BREWER, HE'S BEEN CALLED THE "FATHER OF THE AMERICAN REVOLUTION"	**$1000**	WHO IS

DOUBLE JEOPARDY!

AMERICAN REVOLUTIONARIES

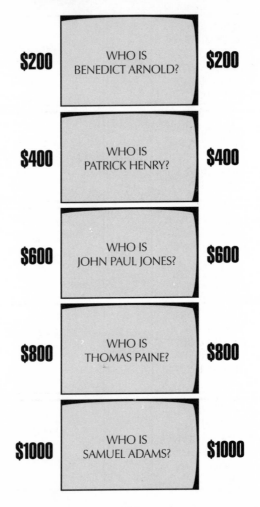

$200 — WHO IS BENEDICT ARNOLD? — $200

$400 — WHO IS PATRICK HENRY? — $400

$600 — WHO IS JOHN PAUL JONES? — $600

$800 — WHO IS THOMAS PAINE? — $800

$1000 — WHO IS SAMUEL ADAMS? — $1000

DOUBLE JEOPARDY!

BEFORE & AFTER

1970s SITCOM BIGOT ON WHOM THE COLONISTS FOUGHT AN IMPORTANT REVOLUTIONARY WAR BATTLE	**$200**	WHO IS
DISNEY CHIPMUNKS WHO HOOK UP WITH THE QUEEN OF THE WEST	**$400**	WHO ARE
"ON THE GOOD SHIP LOLLIPOP" SINGER WHO VISITS INDIANA JONES IN HIS SECOND MOVIE	**$600**	WHO IS
CONTEMPORARY VIRTUOSO CELLIST WHOSE "BOYS" ROBBED BANKS IN THE 1930s	**$800**	WHO IS
STAGE PLAY THAT FEATURES MAGGIE, BIG DADDY & BRICK IN TIBET	**$1000**	WHAT IS

DOUBLE JEOPARDY!

BEFORE & AFTER

$200 — WHO IS ARCHIE BUNKER HILL? — $200

$400 — WHO ARE CHIP & DALE EVANS? — $400

$600 — WHO IS SHIRLEY TEMPLE OF DOOM? — $600

$800 — WHO IS YO-YO MA BARKER? — $800

$1000 — WHAT IS "CAT ON A HOT TIN ROOF OF THE WORLD"? — $1000

FINAL JEOPARDY!

SPORTS

THE FACT THAT HE DIDN'T
PLAY SEPTEMBER 20, 1998
MADE HEADLINES

WHO IS

FINAL JEOPARDY!

SPORTS

WHO IS CAL RIPKEN, JR.?

JEOPARDY!™

What Is Quiz Book 4?

JEOPARDY!

MIDDLE NAME LEE

IN 1998 THIS ACTRESS RETURNED TO THE SCREEN AS LAURIE STRODE IN "HALLOWEEN H2O"	**$100**	WHO IS
CODY & CASSIDY'S MOM	**$200**	WHO IS
SINCE LEAVING VAN HALEN, HE'S RELEASED SUCH SOLO ALBUMS AS "EAT 'EM & SMILE" & "SKYSCRAPER"	**$300**	WHO IS
HIS HIGH-PROFILE CLIENTS HAVE INCLUDED SAM SHEPPARD, PATTY HEARST & O.J. SIMPSON	**$400**	WHO IS
HE'S THE LEGENDARY SINGER & GUITARIST NICKNAMED "THE KING OF THE BOOGIE"	**$500**	WHO IS

JEOPARDY!

MIDDLE NAME LEE

$100 — WHO IS JAMIE LEE CURTIS? — $100

$200 — WHO IS KATHIE LEE GIFFORD? — $200

$300 — WHO IS DAVID LEE ROTH? — $300

$400 — WHO IS F. LEE BAILEY? — $400

$500 — WHO IS JOHN LEE HOOKER? — $500

JEOPARDY!

THE GLOBE

WITH OVER 50 INDE-PENDENT COUNTRIES, THIS CONTINENT HAS MORE THAN ANY OTHER	**$100**	WHAT IS
THE TYRRHENIAN SEA ON ITALY'S WEST COAST IS AN ARM OF THIS SEA	**$200**	WHAT IS
THE EQUATOR CROSSES MORE LAND IN THIS SOUTH AMERICAN NATION THAN ANY OTHER	**$300**	WHAT IS
THE SOUTHERN MIDSECTION OF THIS NATION IS KNOWN AS THE MASSIF CENTRAL	**$400**	WHAT IS
THIS COUNTRY'S NORTHERN BORDER TOUCHES CHINA, BHUTAN & NEPAL	**$500**	WHAT IS

3

JEOPARDY!

THE GLOBE

$100	WHAT IS AFRICA?	**$100**
$200	WHAT IS THE MEDITERRANEAN?	**$200**
$300	WHAT IS BRAZIL?	**$300**
$400	WHAT IS FRANCE?	**$400**
$500	WHAT IS INDIA?	**$500**

4

JEOPARDY!

NATURE

Clue	Value	Response
A BEE DOES IT ABOUT 200 TIMES A SECOND; A MOSQUITO, 500 TIMES A SECOND	**$100**	WHAT IS
THE FLY AGARIC, A DEADLY TYPE OF THIS FUNGUS, WAS ONCE USED TO POISON FLIES	**$200**	WHAT IS
THIS KINGDOM IS COMMONLY DIVIDED INTO VASCULAR, IN-CLUDING CYCADS, & NONVASCULAR, IN-CLUDING HORNWORTS	**$300**	WHAT IS
THE WHELK, A CAR-NIVOROUS MARINE GASTROPOD, HAS A SHELL OF THIS SHAPE	**$400**	WHAT IS
IN A POPULAR SCIENCE EXPERIMENT IODINE ON A PIECE OF POTATO TURNS IT DARK, INDICATING THIS SUBSTANCE IS PRESENT	**$500**	WHAT IS

JEOPARDY!

NATURE

$100	WHAT IS BEAT ITS WINGS?	$100
$200	WHAT IS A MUSHROOM?	$200
$300	WHAT IS THE PLANT KINGDOM?	$300
$400	WHAT IS SPIRAL?	$400
$500	WHAT IS STARCH?	$500

JEOPARDY!

PASTA BAR

Clue	Value	Response
PUTTANESCA IS A ZESTY SAUCE FEATURING CAPERS & THESE PIZZA FISHIES	$100	WHAT ARE
THE REGGIANO TYPE OF THIS HARD, DRY CHEESE IS ONE OF THE BEST FOR GRATING OVER PASTA	$200	WHAT IS
ORECCHIETTE ARE SHAPED LIKE THESE HUMAN ORGANS, BUT PEOPLE EAT THEM ANYWAY	$300	WHAT ARE
AGLIO E OLIO, ONE OF THE SIMPLEST SAUCES, MAINLY CONSISTS OF HEATED OLIVE OIL & THIS	$400	WHAT IS
THIS PASTA LOOKS KIND OF SQUIGGLY— APPROPRIATELY, SINCE ITS NAME MEANS "LITTLE WORMS"	$500	WHAT IS

JEOPARDY!

PASTA BAR

$100	WHAT ARE ANCHOVIES?	**$100**
$200	WHAT IS PARMESAN?	**$200**
$300	WHAT ARE EARS?	**$300**
$400	WHAT IS GARLIC?	**$400**
$500	WHAT IS VERMICELLI?	**$500**

JEOPARDY!™

"RED", "WHITE" & "BLUE"

Clue	Value	Response
YOU'LL FIND IT AT 1600 PENNSYLVANIA AVENUE	$100	WHAT IS
WITH POLITICAL ASPIRATIONS, ELIZABETH DOLE RESIGNED AS HEAD OF THIS IN JANUARY 1999	$200	WHAT IS
WHEN WAVED IN THE AIR, IT'S A UNIVERSAL SIGN OF SURRENDER	$300	WHAT IS
IN 2000 THIS TEAM SIGNED DEION SANDERS	$400	WHAT IS
ACCESSIBLE ONLY BY BOAT, IT'S A NATURAL LIMESTONE CAVERN IN THE BAY OF NAPLES	$500	WHAT IS

JEOPARDY!

"RED", "WHITE" & "BLUE"

$100	WHAT IS THE WHITE HOUSE?	$100
$200	WHAT IS THE (AMERICAN) RED CROSS?	$200
$300	WHAT IS A WHITE FLAG?	$300
$400	WHAT IS THE WASHINGTON REDSKINS?	$400
$500	WHAT IS THE BLUE GROTTO?	$500

JEOPARDY!

CALAMITY JANE

JANE HAD SOME "DARK" TIMES AS A CAMP FOLLOWER OF AN EXPEDITION TO THESE SOUTH DAKOTA HILLS	**$100**	WHAT ARE
JANE'S JOB TITLE OF BULLWHACKER INDICATES SHE DROVE CATTLE WITH ONE OF THESE IMPLEMENTS	**$200**	WHAT IS
GENERAL GEORGE, WHOSE TROOPS JANE RODE WITH, HAD THIS LAST NAME THAT NIXON SAID DIDN'T APPLY TO HIM	**$300**	WHAT IS
A WOMAN SURFACED IN 1941 CLAIMING TO BE THE DAUGHTER OF JANE & THIS MAN WHO PLAYED ONE POKER HAND TOO MANY	**$400**	WHO IS
JANE'S GIG AT THE 1901 PAN-AMERICAN EXPO IN THIS CITY WAS OVERSHADOWED BY THE McKINLEY ASSASSINATION THERE	**$500**	WHAT IS

JEOPARDY!

CALAMITY JANE

$100   WHAT ARE THE BLACK HILLS?   **$100**

$200   WHAT IS A (BULL)WHIP?   **$200**

$300   WHAT IS CROOK?   **$300**

$400   WHO IS WILD BILL HICKOK?   **$400**

$500   WHAT IS BUFFALO?   **$500**

DOUBLE JEOPARDY!

ANCIENT ANIMALS

BEFORE THIS ANIMAL BECAME COMMON, ROMANS USED THE FERRET FOR VERMIN CONTROL	**$200**	WHAT IS
HERODOTUS TOLD THE TALE OF ARION'S RESCUE AT SEA BY ONE OF THESE MAMMALS	**$400**	WHAT IS
A JAPANESE FOLKTALE TELLS OF URASHIMA TARO WHO SAVES ONE OF THESE SEA REPTILES THAT TURNS INTO A YOUNG WOMAN	**$600**	WHAT IS
THESE ANIMALS WERE INVOLVED IN THE PREMIERE EVENT IN THE FUNERAL GAMES FOR PATROCLUS	**$800**	WHAT ARE
THE "LUCANIAN COWS" PYRRHUS USED IN HIS INVASION OF ITALY WERE THESE, FROM ASIA	**$1000**	WHAT ARE

DOUBLE JEOPARDY!

ANCIENT ANIMALS

$200	WHAT IS THE CAT?	$200
$400	WHAT IS A DOLPHIN?	$400
$600	WHAT IS A TURTLE?	$600
$800	WHAT ARE HORSES?	$800
$1000	WHAT ARE ELEPHANTS?	$1000

DOUBLE JEOPARDY!

COLLEGES

IRVIN FELD FOUNDED A COLLEGE IN VENICE, FLORIDA IN 1968 TO TRAIN THESE PERFORMERS FOR THE CIRCUS	**$200**	WHAT ARE
MESA STATE IS A COLLEGE IN GRAND JUNCTION IN THIS STATE	**$400**	WHAT IS
A COLLEGE OF PODIATRY IN CHICAGO IS NAMED FOR THIS DOCTOR	**$600**	WHO IS
THE GRADUATES OF THIS OWATONNA, MINNESOTA BAPTIST BIBLE COLLEGE MUST BE POPPIN' FRESH (WE COULDN'T RESIST THE JOKE)	**$800**	WHAT IS
LOCATED IN CHARLESTON, IT'S "THE MILITARY COLLEGE OF SOUTH CAROLINA"	**$1000**	WHAT IS

DOUBLE JEOPARDY!

COLLEGES

$200	WHAT ARE CLOWNS?	**$200**
$400	WHAT IS COLORADO?	**$400**
$600	WHO IS DR. WILLIAM M. SCHOLL?	**$600**
$800	WHAT IS PILLSBURY (BAPTIST BIBLE COLLEGE)?	**$800**
$1000	WHAT IS THE CITADEL?	**$1000**

DOUBLE JEOPARDY!

ON CD

ON THE COVER OF THIS DUO'S BOXED SET "OLD FRIENDS", A CIGARETTE HAS BEEN AIRBRUSHED OUT OF PAUL'S FINGERS	**$200**	WHO ARE
MADONNA TOLD THESE "STORIES" ON A 1994 CD	**$400**	WHAT ARE
"THE REAL SLIM SHADY" APPEARS ON THE CD OF THIS RAPPER'S "MARSHALL MATHERS LP"	**$600**	WHO IS
THIS NIRVANA CD TITLE IS FOUND IN THE LYRICS OF "SMELLS LIKE TEEN SPIRIT"	**$800**	WHAT IS
"PERSONAL JESUS" & "ENJOY THE SILENCE" ARE ON A 1998 COMPILATION BY THIS ENGLISH BAND WITH A FRENCH NAME	**$1000**	WHAT IS

DOUBLE JEOPARDY!

ON CD

$200	WHO ARE SIMON & GARFUNKEL?	**$200**
$400	WHAT ARE BEDTIME STORIES?	**$400**
$600	WHO IS EMINEM?	**$600**
$800	WHAT IS "NEVERMIND"?	**$800**
$1000	WHAT IS DEPECHE MODE?	**$1000**

DOUBLE JEOPARDY!

LITERATURE

Clue	Value	Response
A 1927 BOOK OF SHORT STORIES BY ERNEST HEMINGWAY WAS TITLED "MEN WITHOUT" THESE	**$200**	WHAT ARE
POET WHO WROTE, "BEFORE I BUILT A WALL I'D ASK TO KNOW WHAT I WAS WALLING IN OR WALLING OUT"	**$400**	WHO IS
IN JAMES FENIMORE COOPER'S "THE PIO-NEERS" OLIVER EDWARDS IS THIS "NATTY" FRONTIERS-MAN'S COMPANION	**$600**	WHO IS
THE FATHER OF THIS "GOOD-BYE, MR. CHIPS" AUTHOR WAS A SCHOOLTEACHER, NOT A HOTELIER	**$800**	WHO IS
BALZAC WROTE "LA COMEDIE HUMAINE" IN THE 1840s & THIS AMERICAN WROTE "THE HUMAN COM-EDY" IN THE 1940s	**$1000**	WHO IS

DOUBLE JEOPARDY!

LITERATURE

$200	WHAT ARE "WOMEN"?	$200
$400	WHO IS ROBERT FROST?	$400
$600	WHO IS NATTY BUMPPO?	$600
$800	WHO IS JAMES HILTON?	$800
$1000	WHO IS WILLIAM SAROYAN?	$1000

DOUBLE JEOPARDY!

AIRPORT PEOPLE

AN ORANGE COUNTY, CALIFORNIA AIRPORT IS NAMED FOR THIS "DUKE" OF THE MOVIES	**$200**	WHO IS
THIS MAN FOR WHOM A BUSY MIDWESTERN AIRPORT IS NAMED WAS A WWII FLYING HERO	**$400**	WHO IS
WASHINGTON, D.C. HAS AN AIRPORT NAMED FOR THIS '50s SECRETARY OF STATE	**$600**	WHO IS
THE NAME OF THIS RENAISSANCE PAINTER/SCULPTOR/ ARCHITECT/BOTANIST/ MATHEMATICIAN IS ON ROME'S AIRPORT	**$800**	WHO IS
IT'S THE NEW YORK CITY AIRPORT NAMED FOR A FORMER NEW YORK CITY MAYOR	**$1000**	WHAT IS

DOUBLE JEOPARDY!

AIRPORT PEOPLE

$200 — WHO IS JOHN WAYNE? — $200

$400 — WHO IS EDWARD "BUTCH" O'HARE? — $400

$600 — WHO IS JOHN FOSTER DULLES? — $600

$800 — WHO IS LEONARDO DA VINCI? — $800

$1000 — WHAT IS LaGUARDIA? — $1000

DOUBLE JEOPARDY!

QUASI-RELATED PAIRS

Clue	Value	Response
A MIXED FRUIT JUICE BEVERAGE & MISS GARLAND	**$200**	WHAT IS
THE SINGER OF "RING OF FIRE" & THE STAR OF "ME, MYSELF & IRENE"	**$400**	WHO ARE
AN ETHNIC GROUP OF NORTHERN IRAQ & A TYPE OF HIGHWAY "STATION" FOR TRUCKERS	**$600**	WHAT ARE
AN ENGLISH EMPIRICAL PHILOSOPHER & THE AUTHOR OF "THE STAR-SPANGLED BANNER"	**$800**	WHO ARE
SLANG TERM FOR A GUY FROM SYDNEY & THE VETERINARIAN AUTHOR OF "ALL CREATURES GREAT AND SMALL"	**$1000**	WHO ARE

DOUBLE JEOPARDY!

QUASI-RELATED PAIRS

$200	WHAT IS PUNCH & JUDY?	**$200**
$400	WHO ARE CASH & CARREY?	**$400**
$600	WHAT ARE KURDS & WEIGH?	**$600**
$800	WHO ARE LOCKE AND KEY?	**$800**
$1000	WHO ARE AUSSIE & HERRIOT?	**$1000**

2 OF THE 3 NBA TEAMS
WHOSE NAMES DON'T
END WITH THE LETTER S

WHAT ARE

FINAL JEOPARDY!

BASKETBALL

WHAT ARE THE
MIAMI HEAT,
ORLANDO MAGIC
& UTAH JAZZ?

JEOPARDY!

DID THEY MOVE IT?

STUTTGART IS A LITTLE WAYS FROM LITTLE ROCK IN THIS STATE	**$100**	WHAT IS
YOU'LL FIND LAKE GENEVA IF YOU HEAD DUE WEST FROM KENOSHA IN THIS STATE	**$200**	WHAT IS
AS WELL AS IN CALIFORNIA, THERE'S A LOS ANGELES ABOUT 200 MILES SOUTH OF SANTIAGO IN THIS COUNTRY	**$300**	WHAT IS
IT MAKES SENSE THAT INVERNESS IS IN THIS CANADIAN ATLANTIC PROVINCE	**$400**	WHAT IS
YOU'LL FIND A BUENOS AIRES IN THIS COUNTRY THAT'S JUST NORTH OF PANAMA	**$500**	WHAT IS

JEOPARDY!

DID THEY MOVE IT?

$100 — WHAT IS ARKANSAS? — $100

$200 — WHAT IS WISCONSIN? — $200

$300 — WHAT IS CHILE? — $300

$400 — WHAT IS NOVA SCOTIA? — $400

$500 — WHAT IS COSTA RICA? — $500

JEOPARDY!

I HEARD THE "NEWS"

CANINE TERM FOR AN INQUISITIVE REPORTER	**$100**	WHAT IS
THESE SHORT FILMS OF CURRENT EVENTS, SUCH AS "THE MARCH OF TIME" SERIES, PLAYED IN MOVIE HOUSES IN THE '40s	**$200**	WHAT ARE
IN 2000 IT HAD CONSECUTIVE COVERS ON SUPREME COURT CONTROVERSIES & HARRY POTTER	**$300**	WHAT IS
IT'S THE INEXPENSIVE PAPER MADE FROM WOOD PULP OF WHICH YOUR MORNING PAPER IS MADE	**$400**	WHAT IS
THIS RUPERT MURDOCH COMPANY OWNS THE L.A. DODGERS, THE NEW YORK POST & FOX STUDIOS	**$500**	WHAT IS

JEOPARDY!

I HEARD THE "NEWS"

$100	WHAT IS NEWSHOUND?	$100
$200	WHAT ARE NEWSREELS?	$200
$300	WHAT IS "NEWSWEEK"?	$300
$400	WHAT IS NEWSPRINT?	$400
$500	WHAT IS NEWS CORPORATION?	$500

JEOPARDY!

U.S. HISTORY

RADICAL REPUBLICANS IMPEACHED & TRIED TO REMOVE THIS PRESIDENT IN 1868	$100	WHO IS
THIS AVUNCULAR NICKNAME FOR THE GOVERNMENT WAS COINED BY THOSE AGAINST THE WAR OF 1812	$200	WHAT IS
WHEN EAST & WEST WERE LINKED BY THIS IN OCTOBER 1861, THE DAYS OF THE PONY EXPRESS WERE NUMBERED	$300	WHAT IS
IN 1851 STONEWALL JACKSON BECAME AN INSTRUCTOR AT VMI, THIS SCHOOL	$400	WHAT IS
THIS SECRETARY OF STATE RETIRED IN 1869, 2 YEARS AFTER HIS "FOLLY"	$500	WHO IS

31

JEOPARDY!
U.S. HISTORY

$100   WHO IS ANDREW JOHNSON?   **$100**

$200   WHAT IS UNCLE SAM?   **$200**

$300   WHAT IS THE TELEGRAPH?   **$300**

$400   WHAT IS THE VIRGINIA MILITARY INSTITUTE?   **$400**

$500   WHO IS WILLIAM SEWARD?   **$500**

JEOPARDY!

PALINDROMIC WORDS

WHEN MALES TAKE ON FEMALES, IT'S CALLED "THE BATTLE OF" THESE	**$100**	WHAT ARE
AIR TRAFFIC CONTROLLERS CHECK THIS SCREEN TO GET THE DISH ON THE FLIGHT PATH OF A PLANE	**$200**	WHAT IS
A CARPENTER'S TOOL, OR THE TYPE OF "HEAD" A SENSIBLE PERSON HAS	**$300**	WHAT IS
THIS ESKIMO CANOE IS STEERED WITH A DOUBLE-BLADED PADDLE	**$400**	WHAT IS
MAJOR LEAGUE PITCHERS DREAD INJURY TO THIS "CUFF"	**$500**	WHAT IS

JEOPARDY!

PALINDROMIC WORDS

$100 — WHAT ARE THE SEXES? — $100

$200 — WHAT IS RADAR? — $200

$300 — WHAT IS LEVEL? — $300

$400 — WHAT IS A KAYAK? — $400

$500 — WHAT IS ROTATOR? — $500

JEOPARDY!

CRITTERS

THIS BEAR, URSUS MARITIMUS, SPENDS MUCH OF ITS TIME ON ICE FLOES & MAY BEAR ITS YOUNG ON THEM	**$100**	WHAT IS
THE RUBY-THROATED SPECIES OF THIS BIRD USUALLY LAYS 2 TINY EGGS ABOUT THE SIZE OF NAVY BEANS	**$200**	WHAT IS
GORILLAS RARELY WALK UPRIGHT, BUT USUALLY SUPPORT THEIR UPPER BODIES BY WALKING ON THESE HAND PARTS	**$300**	WHAT ARE
THIS ARMORED MAMMAL IS ONE OF THE FEW KNOWN ANIMAL HOSTS FOR THE BACTERIUM THAT CAUSES LEPROSY IN HUMANS	**$400**	WHAT IS
THE LARGEST TYPE OF THIS TAILED AMPHIBIAN IN THE U.S. IS THE HELLBENDER, WHICH MAY REACH 3 FEET	**$500**	WHAT IS

JEOPARDY!

CRITTERS

$100	WHAT IS THE POLAR BEAR?	$100
$200	WHAT IS THE HUMMINGBIRD?	$200
$300	WHAT ARE KNUCKLES?	$300
$400	WHAT IS THE ARMADILLO?	$400
$500	WHAT IS THE SALAMANDER?	$500

JEOPARDY!

PEOPLE

IN THE '60s HIS TRADEMARKS WERE JEWELED COSTUMES & ELABORATELY DESIGNED PIANOS TOPPED BY CANDELABRA	**$100**	WHO IS
IN 1998 SUPERMODEL REBECCA ROMIJN MARRIED THIS FORMER STAR OF TV's "FULL HOUSE"	**$200**	WHO IS
IN 2000 THIS WOMAN WHO WANTED TO MARRY A MULTI-MILLIONAIRE TOOK IT OFF FOR PLAYBOY MAGAZINE	**$300**	WHO IS
THIS "FAST CAR" SINGER HONED HER STYLE ON THE BOSTON CIRCUIT WHILE A STUDENT AT TUFTS UNIVERSITY	**$400**	WHO IS
SOMEDAY, THIS YOUNGER BROTHER OF PRINCE WILLIAM MIGHT WANT TO FORGET HIS DAYS AS A SPICE GIRLS FAN	**$500**	WHO IS

JEOPARDY!

PEOPLE

$100	WHO IS LIBERACE?	**$100**
$200	WHO IS JOHN STAMOS?	**$200**
$300	WHO IS DARVA CONGER?	**$300**
$400	WHO IS TRACY CHAPMAN?	**$400**
$500	WHO IS PRINCE HARRY?	**$500**

DOUBLE JEOPARDY!

RUSSIAN "T" ROOM

HIS WRITING CAREER BEGAN WITH THE SHORT NOVEL "DETSTVO" IN 1852; THE MUCH LONGER PIECES CAME LATER	**$200**	WHO IS
THE TAIGA IS THE FOREST LAND OF RUSSIA & THIS IS ITS NEARLY TREELESS NORTHERN BELT	**$400**	WHAT IS
IN 1919 HE & LENIN FOUNDED THE THIRD INTERNATIONAL TO BRING TOGETHER COMRADES FROM AROUND THE WORLD	**$600**	WHO IS
A GROUP OF 3 IN POWER, OR A VEHICLE DRAWN BY 3 HORSES ABREAST	**$800**	WHAT IS
IN 1992 THIS NEWS AGENCY ADDED ITAR TO ITS NAME, FOR THE INFORMATION-TELEGRAPH AGENCY OF RUSSIA	**$1000**	WHAT IS

DOUBLE JEOPARDY!

RUSSIAN "T" ROOM

$200   WHO IS LEO TOLSTOY? $200

$400   WHAT IS THE TUNDRA? $400

$600   WHO IS LEON TROTSKY? $600

$800   WHAT IS A TROIKA? $800

$1000   WHAT IS TASS? $1000

DOUBLE JEOPARDY!

THE ARTISTIC TOUCH

Clue	Value	Response
THIS ART PRACTICED BY WILLIAM BLAKE PRECEDES "PRINTING" IN THE NAME OF A U.S. BUREAU	$200	WHAT IS
TO FILM JACKSON POLLOCK AT WORK, YOU'D SAY "LIGHTS! CAMERA!" THIS TYPE OF PAINTING	$400	WHAT IS
IN THE 1880s THIS ARTIST WITH "NOIR" IN HIS NAME BROKE WITH IMPRESSIONISM & BEGAN USING MORE BLACK	$600	WHO IS
THE INITIALS OF THIS BRITISH SEASCAPE WHIZ STOOD FOR JOSEPH MALLORD WILLIAM	$800	WHO IS
LAST NAME OF FORMER HUSBAND & WIFE WALTER & MARGARET, KNOWN FOR PAINTING LARGE-EYED WAIFS	$1000	WHAT IS

DOUBLE JEOPARDY!

THE ARTISTIC TOUCH

$200	WHAT IS ENGRAVING?	**$200**
$400	WHAT IS ACTION PAINTING?	**$400**
$600	WHO IS PIERRE-AUGUSTE RENOIR?	**$600**
$800	WHO IS J.M.W. TURNER?	**$800**
$1000	WHAT IS KEANE?	**$1000**

42

DOUBLE JEOPARDY!

FLYING

Clue	Value	Response
IN HIS FIRST STORIES, HE WAS ABLE TO "LEAP TALL BUILDINGS AT A SINGLE BOUND"; HE DIDN'T FLY UNTIL LATER	**$200**	WHO IS
A FLAT ONE NEEDS A TAIL TO SUPPLY DRAG & TO KEEP IT POINTED TO THE SKY	**$400**	WHAT IS
"HE FLIES THROUGH THE AIR WITH THE GREATEST OF EASE", THE DARING YOUNG MAN ON THIS APPARATUS	**$600**	WHAT IS
THIS "ARCTIC" BIRD, STERNA PARADISAEA, BREEDS ON THE COASTS OF NORTH AMERICA BUT MAKES ITS WINTER HOME IN THE ANTARCTIC	**$800**	WHAT IS
ON NOV. 20, 1953, IN A DOUGLAS D-558-2, SCOTT CROSSFIELD FIRST REACHED THIS SPEED	**$1000**	WHAT IS

DOUBLE JEOPARDY!

FLYING

$200	WHO IS SUPERMAN?	**$200**
$400	WHAT IS A KITE?	**$400**
$600	WHAT IS THE FLYING TRAPEZE?	**$600**
$800	WHAT IS THE ARCTIC TERN?	**$800**
$1000	WHAT IS MACH 2?	**$1000**

44

DOUBLE JEOPARDY!

NEXT IN LINE, PLEASE

YEAR, DECADE, CENTURY ...	**$200**	WHAT IS
TAFT, WILSON, HARDING ...	**$400**	WHO IS
IOTA, KAPPA, LAMBDA ...	**$600**	WHAT IS
TENDERFOOT, SECOND CLASS, FIRST CLASS ...	**$800**	WHAT IS
PENNSYLVANIAN PERIOD, PERMIAN PERIOD, TRIASSIC PERIOD ...	**$1000**	WHAT IS

DOUBLE JEOPARDY!

NEXT IN LINE, PLEASE

$200   WHAT IS MILLENNIUM?   **$200**

$400   WHO IS (CALVIN) COOLIDGE?   **$400**

$600   WHAT IS MU?   **$600**

$800   WHAT IS STAR (SCOUT)?   **$800**

$1000   WHAT IS THE JURASSIC PERIOD?   **$1000**

46

DOUBLE JEOPARDY!

THE CINEMA

THIS BEATLE NOT ONLY STARRED IN "GIVE MY REGARDS TO BROAD STREET", HE WROTE THE SCREEN-PLAY & THE SCORE	**$200**	WHO IS
ADS FOR THIS 2000 HORROR SPOOF READ, "NO MERCY. NO SHAME. NO SEQUEL."	**$400**	WHAT IS
"TITANIC" TIED THIS 1959 FILM'S RECORD OF 11 OSCARS BUT DIDN'T OVERTAKE IT	**$600**	WHAT IS
AS A CHILD, THIS "DOCTOR ZHIVAGO" CO-STAR HAD A BIT ROLE IN HER FATHER'S FILM "LIMELIGHT"	**$800**	WHO IS
WE DON'T KNOW WHICH EXECUTIVE "GREEN-LIT" THIS 1999 FILM STARRING SARAH POLLEY & SCOTT WOLF	**$1000**	WHAT IS

DOUBLE JEOPARDY!

THE CINEMA

$200 WHO IS PAUL McCARTNEY? $200

$400 WHAT IS "SCARY MOVIE"? $400

$600 WHAT IS "BEN-HUR"? $600

$800 WHO IS GERALDINE CHAPLIN? $800

$1000 WHAT IS "GO"? $1000

48

DOUBLE JEOPARDY!

POE FOLKS

"I WAS A CHILD AND SHE WAS A CHILD, IN THIS KINGDOM BY THE SEA, BUT WE LOVED WITH A LOVE THAT WAS MORE THAN LOVE, I" & SHE	**$200**	WHO IS
LAST NAME OF RODERICK & HIS SISTER MADELINE, WHO FALL DEAD JUST BEFORE THEIR HOUSE FALLS INTO A MOUNTAIN LAKE	**$400**	WHAT IS
THIS MASKED APPARITION JOINS PRINCE PROSPERO & HIS FRIENDS AT A COSTUME BALL IN A SECLUDED CASTLE	**$600**	WHAT IS
THIS SCHOLARLY AMATEUR DETECTIVE SOLVES THE BAFFLING CASE OF "THE PURLOINED LETTER"	**$800**	WHO IS
HIS "NARRATIVE" RECOUNTS HIS ADVENTURES ON THE GRAMPUS AS IT SAILS FROM NANTUCKET TO THE SOUTH SEAS	**$1000**	WHO IS

DOUBLE JEOPARDY!

POE FOLKS

$200 WHO IS ANNABEL LEE? **$200**

$400 WHAT IS USHER? **$400**

$600 WHAT IS THE RED DEATH? **$600**

$800 WHO IS C. AUGUSTE DUPIN? **$800**

$1000 WHO IS A. GORDON PYM? **$1000**

FINAL JEOPARDY!

'90s TRENDS

THIS ADORNMENT
WAS SEEN ON CHER,
DENNIS RODMAN &
THE 5,000-YEAR-OLD
"ICEMAN" FOUND IN 1991

WHAT IS

FINAL JEOPARDY!

'90s TRENDS

WHAT IS A TATTOO?

JEOPARDY!

FLAGS

Clue	Value	Response
THIS CANADIAN PROVINCE'S FLAG SHOWS THE SETTING SUN & WAVY BLUE BARS REPRESENTING THE PACIFIC OCEAN	**$100**	WHAT IS
FRANCE'S TRICOLOR FLAG FEATURES RED & BLUE—THE COLORS OF PARIS—& THIS, THE ROYAL COLOR OF THE BOURBON KINGS	**$200**	WHAT IS
FLAG FANS MISS THE WACKED-OUT OIL-WELL-IN-THE-MOUN-TAINS PICTURE ON THIS EUROPEAN FLAG IN ITS COMMUNIST DAYS	**$300**	WHAT IS
THIS STATE'S FLAG FEATURES A MOTHER PELICAN WITH ITS YOUNG	**$400**	WHAT IS
THE STAFF & HAT OF THE BISHOP OF URGEL CAN BE FOUND ON THIS TINY PYRENEES COUNTRY'S FLAG	**$500**	WHAT IS

53

JEOPARDY!

FLAGS

$100	WHAT IS BRITISH COLUMBIA?	$100
$200	WHAT IS WHITE?	$200
$300	WHAT IS ROMANIA?	$300
$400	WHAT IS LOUISIANA?	$400
$500	WHAT IS ANDORRA?	$500

JEOPARDY!

GORDONS

Clue	Value	Response
BEFORE HE WAS THE LEAD SINGER OF THE POLICE, HE WAS A TEACHER NAMED GORDON SUMNER	**$100**	WHO IS
THIS BRAWNY FICTIONAL SPACE HERO WAS A YALE GRADUATE & A WORLD-CLASS POLO PLAYER	**$200**	WHO IS
DJ VENUS FLYTRAP WAS THE ALTER EGO OF GORDON SIMS ON THIS SITCOM	**$300**	WHAT IS
HIS HIT SONGS INCLUDE "SUNDOWN" & "THE WRECK OF THE EDMUND FITZGERALD"	**$400**	WHO IS
IN APRIL 1977 JIMMY CARTER COMMUTED HIS SENTENCE TO 8 YEARS, ALLOWING HIM TO BE PAROLED LATER THAT YEAR	**$500**	WHO IS

JEOPARDY!

GORDONS

$100   WHO IS STING? $100

$200   WHO IS FLASH GORDON? $200

$300   WHAT IS "WKRP IN CINCINNATI"? $300

$400   WHO IS GORDON LIGHTFOOT? $400

$500   WHO IS G. GORDON LIDDY? $500

JEOPARDY!

LITHUANIAN HISTORY

EVEN WITHOUT A PROCLAMATION FROM LINCOLN, MANY LITHUANIAN SERFS WERE GIVEN THIS AROUND 1861	**$100**	WHAT IS
LITHUANIA & THESE 2 OTHER BALTIC REPUBLICS LEFT THE SOVIET UNION IN 1991	**$200**	WHAT ARE
IN THE 1860s A RUSSIFICATION PROGRAM MEANT LITHUANIAN BOOKS HAD TO USE THIS RUSSIAN ALPHABET	**$300**	WHAT IS
"TAUTISKA GIESME", WRITTEN IN THE 19th CENTURY BY VINCAS KUDIRKA, BECAME THIS NATIONAL SYMBOL	**$400**	WHAT IS
AN "EARLY" NATIONALIST NEWS-PAPER WAS CALLED AUSRA, MEANING THIS TIME OF DAY	**$500**	WHAT IS

JEOPARDY!

LITHUANIAN HISTORY

$100	WHAT IS EMANCIPATION?	$100
$200	WHAT ARE ESTONIA & LATVIA?	$200
$300	WHAT IS THE CYRILLIC ALPHABET?	$300
$400	WHAT IS THE LITHUANIAN NATIONAL ANTHEM?	$400
$500	WHAT IS DAWN?	$500

JEOPARDY!

DEMOCRATS

THIS FORMER HOOPS STAR CHALLENGED AL GORE FOR THE 2000 DEMOCRATIC NOMINATION	**$100**	WHO IS
IN 1998 JOHN CONYERS WAS REELECTED WITH 87% OF THE VOTE IN THIS STATE'S 14th CONGRESSIONAL DISTRICT	**$200**	WHAT IS
HE DIDN'T OFFICIALLY MEET WITH HIS CABINET FOR THE FIRST 2 YEARS OF HIS TERM, PREFERRING HIS "KITCHEN CABINET"	**$300**	WHO IS
IN 1998 TOM HARKIN & THIS TOM, THE SENATE'S DEMOCRATIC LEADER, CHAIRED A HEARING ON HOG PRICES	**$400**	WHO IS
THIS DEMOCRAT'S "CROSS OF GOLD" SPEECH SUPPORTED THE BIMETALLIC THEORY	**$500**	WHO IS

JEOPARDY!

DEMOCRATS

$100
WHO IS
BILL BRADLEY?
$100

$200
WHAT IS
MICHIGAN?
$200

$300
WHO IS
ANDREW JACKSON?
$300

$400
WHO IS
TOM DASCHLE?
$400

$500
WHO IS WILLIAM
JENNINGS BRYAN?
$500

JEOPARDY!

LOGO LADIES

THIS MINNESOTA-BASED BUTTER MAKER USES AN INDIAN MAIDEN AS ITS TRADEMARK	**$100**	WHAT IS
BILLBOARDS FOR "LITTLE MISS" THIS SUNTAN LOTION BECAME MIAMI LANDMARKS IN THE '50s	**$200**	WHAT IS
IN 1915 LORRAINE COLLETT OF FRESNO BECAME THE ORIGINAL MODEL FOR THIS BRAND OF RAISINS	**$300**	WHAT IS
THE SYMBOL OF THIS MOVIE COMPANY FOUNDED BY HARRY COHN GOT A MAKE-OVER IN 1993	**$400**	WHAT IS
DEBRA McKEE, FOR WHOM THESE SNACK CAKES WERE NAMED, GREW UP TO BE A DIRECTOR OF THE COMPANY THAT MAKES THEM	**$500**	WHAT ARE

JEOPARDY!

LOGO LADIES

$100   WHAT IS LAND O'LAKES?   **$100**

$200   WHAT IS COPPERTONE?   **$200**

$300   WHAT IS SUN-MAID?   **$300**

$400   WHAT IS COLUMBIA PICTURES?   **$400**

$500   WHAT ARE LITTLE DEBBIE (SNACK CAKES)?   **$500**

JEOPARDY!

"BAG" 'EM UP

Clue	Value	Response
IT'S WHERE TIGER CAN KEEP HIS IRONS & DRIVERS & TEES, OH MY!	$100	WHAT IS
BELLOWING HIGHLAND INSTRUMENT	$200	WHAT ARE
IT'S A MIDDLE EAST CAPITAL	$300	WHAT IS
DERIVED FROM THE ITALIAN FOR "LITTLE STICK", IT'S A LONG, NARROW LOAF OF FRENCH BREAD	$400	WHAT IS
A TRIFLE, OR A SHORT PIECE OF MUSIC	$500	WHAT IS

JEOPARDY!

"BAG" 'EM UP

| $100 | WHAT IS A GOLF BAG? | $100 |

| $200 | WHAT ARE THE BAGPIPES? | $200 |

| $300 | WHAT IS BAGHDAD? | $300 |

| $400 | WHAT IS A BAGUETTE? | $400 |

| $500 | WHAT IS A BAGATELLE? | $500 |

DOUBLE JEOPARDY!

QUOTABLE DEFINITIONS

JOHN MASON BROWN'S FAMOUS DEFINITION OF THIS IS "CHEWING GUM FOR THE EYES"	**$200**	WHAT IS
HISTORIAN BRUCE CATTON CALLED THIS SPORT "THE GREATEST CONVERSATION PIECE EVER INVENTED IN AMERICA"	**$400**	WHAT IS
SAMUEL JOHNSON DEFINED THIS SENTIMENT AS "THE LAST REFUGE OF A SCOUNDREL"	**$600**	WHAT IS
AUTHOR WHO DEFINED A CLASSIC AS "A BOOK WHICH PEOPLE PRAISE AND DON'T READ"	**$800**	WHO IS
SHAKESPEARE WROTE IT "IS A PIPE BLOWN BY SURMISES, JEALOUSIES, CONJECTURES"; BUT THAT'S JUST WHAT HE HEARD	**$1000**	WHAT IS

DOUBLE JEOPARDY!
QUOTABLE DEFINITIONS

$200	WHAT IS TELEVISION?	**$200**
$400	WHAT IS BASEBALL?	**$400**
$600	WHAT IS PATRIOTISM?	**$600**
$800	WHO IS MARK TWAIN?	**$800**
$1000	WHAT IS RUMOR?	**$1000**

DOUBLE JEOPARDY!

NORTH DAKOTA

Clue	Value	Response
THE STATE CAPITOL IN THIS CITY IS SOMETIMES CALLED "THE SKYSCRAPER OF THE PRAIRIE"	**$200**	WHAT IS
NORTH DAKOTA BECAME A STATE ON NOVEMBER 2, 1889, THE SAME DAY AS THIS OTHER STATE	**$400**	WHAT IS
SHE JOINED THE LEWIS & CLARK EXPEDITION IN WHAT IS NOW NORTH DAKOTA	**$600**	WHO IS
HE SAID, "I WOULD NEVER HAVE BEEN PRESIDENT IF IT HAD NOT BEEN FOR MY EXPERIENCES IN NORTH DAKOTA"	**$800**	WHO IS
THE AUTHOR OF "HONDO" & OTHER WESTERNS, HE WAS BORN IN JAMESTOWN, NORTH DAKOTA	**$1000**	WHO IS

DOUBLE JEOPARDY!

NORTH DAKOTA

$200	WHAT IS BISMARCK?	**$200**
$400	WHAT IS SOUTH DAKOTA?	**$400**
$600	WHO IS SACAJAWEA?	**$600**
$800	WHO IS TEDDY ROOSEVELT?	**$800**
$1000	WHO IS LOUIS L'AMOUR?	**$1000**

DOUBLE JEOPARDY!

THAI FOOD

THE STAPLE FOOD IN THE NORTH OF THAILAND IS THE STICKY OR GLUTINOUS TYPE OF THIS	**$200**	WHAT IS
TOM KHA KAI IS A CHICKEN SOUP FLAVORED WITH THE "MILK" OF THIS	**$400**	WHAT IS
IN THE NAMES OF NOODLE DISHES, THIS WORD PRECEDES "THAI", "SEE EW" & "WOON SEN"	**$600**	WHAT IS
YOU MIGHT WISH THE SKEWER OF CHICKEN OR BEEF SERVED WITH PEANUT SAUCE WAS "JUST A LITTLE BIT LONGER"	**$800**	WHAT IS
LIKE SOUTHERN COOKING, THAI-AMERICAN CUISINE FEATURES THIS BE"WHISKERED" CREATURE, DEEP-FRIED	**$1000**	WHAT IS

DOUBLE JEOPARDY!

THAI FOOD

$200   WHAT IS RICE?   **$200**

$400   WHAT IS COCONUT?   **$400**

$600   WHAT IS PAD?   **$600**

$800   WHAT IS A SATAY?   **$800**

$1000   WHAT IS CATFISH?   **$1000**

DOUBLE JEOPARDY!

THE THEATRE

LAURENCE HARVEY REIGNED IN THIS REGAL ROLE IN THE 1964 LONDON PRODUCTION OF "CAMELOT"	**$200**	WHO IS
NOEL COWARD'S 1947 DRAMA "PEACE IN OUR TIME" DEPICTS LIFE IN ENGLAND IF THIS DICTATOR HAD CONQUERED IT	**$400**	WHO IS
CHEKHOV'S "THREE SISTERS" DREAM OF GOING TO THIS CAPITAL CITY	**$600**	WHAT IS
SEWAMONO PLAYS ARE DOMESTIC DRAMAS ABOUT MIDDLE-CLASS LIFE IN THIS FORM OF JAPANESE DRAMA	**$800**	WHAT IS
IN 1999 CRITICS LAMBASTED "TALLER THAN A DWARF", WRITTEN BY THIS EX-PARTNER OF MIKE NICHOLS	**$1000**	WHO IS

DOUBLE JEOPARDY!

THE THEATRE

$200	WHO IS KING ARTHUR?	**$200**
$400	WHO IS ADOLF HITLER?	**$400**
$600	WHAT IS MOSCOW?	**$600**
$800	WHAT IS KABUKI?	**$800**
$1000	WHO IS ELAINE MAY?	**$1000**

DOUBLE JEOPARDY!

THE YEAR OF THE HEADLINE

ORDERS SKYROCKET AS VIAGRA GOES ON THE MARKET!	**$200**	WHAT IS
U.S. ABANDONS SAIGON; VIETNAM WAR ENDS!	**$400**	WHAT IS
OPERATION "DESERT STORM" BEGINS; IRAQ INVADED!	**$600**	WHAT IS
MONDALE NOMINATED FOR U.S. PRESIDENT!	**$800**	WHAT IS
QUEEN VICTORIA SHUFFLES OFF THIS MORTAL COIL!	**$1000**	WHAT IS

DOUBLE JEOPARDY!
THE YEAR OF THE HEADLINE

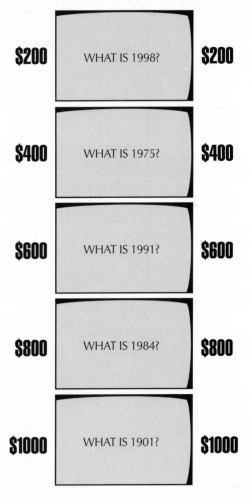

$200   WHAT IS 1998?   **$200**

$400   WHAT IS 1975?   **$400**

$600   WHAT IS 1991?   **$600**

$800   WHAT IS 1984?   **$800**

$1000   WHAT IS 1901?   **$1000**

DOUBLE JEOPARDY!

VANS

COLUMNIST ABIGAIL, OPPOSED TO SMOKING, OR PRESIDENT MARTIN, OPPOSED TO THE ANNEXATION OF TEXAS	**$200**	WHO IS
GAME SHOW PRODUCERS ONCE QUAKED AT THE NAME OF THIS 1950s COLUMBIA UNIVERSITY INSTRUCTOR	**$400**	WHO IS
THIS "MOONDANCE" SINGER WAS ONCE MARRIED TO A WOMAN NAMED JANET PLANET	**$600**	WHO IS
LAST NAME OF "WATERMELON MAN" DIRECTOR MELVIN & HIS SON, "NEW JACK CITY" DIRECTOR MARIO	**$800**	WHAT IS
SHE SET AN AMERICAN RECORD IN 1996 BY SWIMMING THE 50-METER FREESTYLE IN 24.87 SECONDS	**$1000**	WHO IS

DOUBLE JEOPARDY!

VANS

$200	WHO IS VAN BUREN?	**$200**
$400	WHO IS CHARLES VAN DOREN?	**$400**
$600	WHO IS VAN MORRISON?	**$600**
$800	WHAT IS VAN PEEBLES?	**$800**
$1000	WHO IS AMY VAN DYKEN?	**$1000**

FINAL JEOPARDY!

ITALIAN VOCABULARY

THIS WORD WELL KNOWN
TO SCULPTURE LOVERS
CAN BE TRANSLATED AS
"MERCY" OR "COMPASSION"

WHAT IS

FINAL JEOPARDY!
ITALIAN VOCABULARY

WHAT IS PIETA?

JEOPARDY!

THE PC

Clue	Value	Response
BYZANTINE PRIESTS MIGHT KNOW THE NAME OF THESE SCREEN IMAGES THAT CAN REPRESENT PROGRAMS OR FILES	$100	WHAT ARE
ONE OF THESE IS EQUAL TO 1,024 BYTES	$200	WHAT IS
TO TAKE FLEAS OFF YOUR DOG, OR TO DETECT, LOCATE & CORRECT ERRORS IN A COMPUTER PROGRAM	$300	WHAT IS
"SMALL" TERM FOR A CENTRAL PROCESSING UNIT ON ONE INTEGRATED CIRCUIT	$400	WHAT IS
IT'S NOT A SPIDER, IT'S THE PERSON RESPONSIBLE FOR MAINTAINING AN INTERNET SITE	$500	WHAT IS

JEOPARDY!

THE PC

$100	WHAT ARE ICONS?	**$100**
$200	WHAT IS A KILOBYTE?	**$200**
$300	WHAT IS TO DEBUG?	**$300**
$400	WHAT IS A MICROPROCESSOR?	**$400**
$500	WHAT IS A WEBMASTER?	**$500**

JEOPARDY!

AROUND THE PACIFIC

Clue	Value	Response
2 OF CHILE'S JUAN FERNANDEZ ISLANDS ARE NAMED FOR ALEXANDER SELKIRK & THIS FICTIONAL CASTAWAY HE INSPIRED	$100	WHO IS
THIS RIVER IN WASHINGTON & OREGON WAS EXPLORED BY ROBERT GRAY IN A SHIP OF THE SAME NAME	$200	WHAT IS
IN 1697 JESUITS FOUNDED LORETO, THE 1st PERMANENT EUROPEAN SETTLEMENT ON THIS "LOWER" PENINSULA	$300	WHAT IS
THE ISLAND OF MINDANAO IS A MUSLIM CENTER IN THIS MAINLY ROMAN CATHOLIC COUNTRY	$400	WHAT IS
TO CALL THE ROTORUA MAN, YOU'LL HAVE TO RING UP THIS ANTIPODEAN ISLAND NATION	$500	WHAT IS

JEOPARDY!

AROUND THE PACIFIC

$100	WHO IS ROBINSON CRUSOE?	**$100**
$200	WHAT IS THE COLUMBIA?	**$200**
$300	WHAT IS LOWER (OR BAJA) CALIFORNIA?	**$300**
$400	WHAT IS THE PHILIPPINES?	**$400**
$500	WHAT IS NEW ZEALAND?	**$500**

JEOPARDY!

COCKNEY RHYMING SLANG

Clue	Value	Response
IT'S A DICKORY DOCK, WHETHER OR NOT A MOUSE RUNS UP IT	**$100**	WHAT IS
ASK A COCKNEY BARBER FOR A DIG IN THE GRAVE & HE SHOULD GIVE YOU ONE OF THESE	**$200**	WHAT IS
IT'S WHAT A MOTHER HUBBARD IS; HERS WAS BARE, BY THE WAY	**$300**	WHAT IS
A GLASGOW RANGER, THIS KIND OF PERSON, WASN'T WELCOME IN SMALL TOWNS IN THE OLD WEST	**$400**	WHAT IS
COCKNEYS USE THE NAME OF THIS DICKENS TITLE CHARACTER AS RHYMING SLANG FOR A JUDGE	**$500**	WHO IS

JEOPARDY!

COCKNEY RHYMING SLANG

$100	WHAT IS A CLOCK?	$100
$200	WHAT IS A SHAVE?	$200
$300	WHAT IS A CUPBOARD?	$300
$400	WHAT IS A STRANGER?	$400
$500	WHO IS BARNABY RUDGE?	$500

JEOPARDY!

GEOGRAPHIC TERMS

THIS LINE DIVIDES THE EARTH INTO NORTHERN & SOUTHERN HEMISPHERES	**$100**	WHAT IS
TILL IS DEFINED AS THE ROCK MATERIAL DRAGGED UNDER ONE OF THESE AS IT MOVES	**$200**	WHAT IS
A BODY OF WATER USUALLY SMALLER THAN A GULF; BOTANY IS A FAMOUS ONE	**$300**	WHAT IS
NORMALLY, AN ATOLL IS MADE OF THIS OR NOTHING ATOLL	**$400**	WHAT IS
A COMMON PLACE NAME IN THE SOUTHWEST, FROM A SPANISH TERM, IT'S A DRY RIVER BED	**$500**	WHAT IS

85

JEOPARDY!

GEOGRAPHIC TERMS

$100	WHAT IS THE EQUATOR?	**$100**
$200	WHAT IS A GLACIER?	**$200**
$300	WHAT IS A BAY?	**$300**
$400	WHAT IS CORAL?	**$400**
$500	WHAT IS AN ARROYO?	**$500**

JEOPARDY!

SIMONIZING

BORN IN 1927, HE WROTE HIS FIRST BROADWAY HIT, "COME BLOW YOUR HORN", IN 1960	$100	WHO IS
FROM 1972 TO 1983, SHE WAS MRS. JAMES TAYLOR	$200	WHO IS
HARRIET BEECHER STOWE'S SINISTER SLAVER	$300	WHO IS
HE WON THE DEMOCRATIC PRESIDENTIAL PRIMARY IN ILLINOIS IN 1988; NO BIG SURPRISE, HE WAS THEIR SENATOR	$400	WHO IS
HE'S THE LEAD SINGER & OLDEST MEMBER OF DURAN DURAN	$500	WHO IS

JEOPARDY!

SIMONIZING

$100	WHO IS NEIL SIMON?	**$100**
$200	WHO IS CARLY SIMON?	**$200**
$300	WHO IS SIMON LEGREE?	**$300**
$400	WHO IS PAUL SIMON?	**$400**
$500	WHO IS SIMON LE BON?	**$500**

JEOPARDY!

PRESIDENTIAL LAST WORDS

JUST BEFORE COLLAPSING IN 1945, HE REMARKED, "I HAVE A TERRIFIC HEADACHE"	**$100**	WHO IS
"IT IS WELL" WERE HIS LAST WORDS IN 1799	**$200**	WHO IS
IN 1885, HE CROAKED, "WATER!"	**$300**	WHO IS
IN 1969 HE ENDED HIS TOUR OF DUTY WITH "I HAVE ALWAYS LOVED MY COUNTRY"	**$400**	WHO IS
IN 1893 HAYES GASPED, "I KNOW THAT I AM GOING TO WHERE" THIS WIFE "IS"	**$500**	WHO IS

89

JEOPARDY!™

PRESIDENTIAL LAST WORDS

$100 WHO IS FRANKLIN DELANO ROOSEVELT? **$100**

$200 WHO IS GEORGE WASHINGTON? **$200**

$300 WHO IS ULYSSES S. GRANT? **$300**

$400 WHO IS DWIGHT D. EISENHOWER? **$400**

$500 WHO IS LUCY? **$500**

DOUBLE JEOPARDY!

NAMES IN THE LAW

THE CIVIL CODE SET UP IN FRANCE IN 1804 IS ALSO KNOWN AS THIS CODE	**$200**	WHAT IS
EARL WARREN RULED ON THIS MAN'S CASE THAT A SUSPECT MUST BE WARNED PRIOR TO QUESTIONING THAT HE CAN STAY SILENT	**$400**	WHO IS
IN 1970 A WOMAN USED THIS PSEUDONYM WHEN SHE SUED TEXAS D.A. HENRY WADE TO ALLOW HER AN ABORTION	**$600**	WHAT IS
HE TOOK ON FERGUSON IN 1896 AFTER REFUSING TO SIT IN THE RAILROAD CAR FOR BLACKS ONLY	**$800**	WHO IS
THE 1936 ROBINSON-PATMAN ACT REVIVED & REVISED THIS MAN'S ANTITRUST ACT OF 1890	**$1000**	WHO IS

DOUBLE JEOPARDY!

NAMES IN THE LAW

$200 — WHAT IS THE NAPOLEONIC CODE? — **$200**

$400 — WHO IS ERNESTO MIRANDA? — **$400**

$600 — WHAT IS JANE ROE? — **$600**

$800 — WHO IS HOMER PLESSY? — **$800**

$1000 — WHO IS JOHN SHERMAN? — **$1000**

DOUBLE JEOPARDY!

CLASSIC DRAMA

Clue	Value	Response
IT INCLUDES THE FORESHADOWING LINE "HEDDA DARLING—DON'T TOUCH THOSE DANGEROUS THINGS!"	**$200**	WHAT IS
HE'S THE KING OR "REX" WHO SAVES THEBES IN AN ANCIENT WORK BY SOPHOCLES	**$400**	WHO IS
PIERRE CORNEILLE WROTE A 1637 PLAY ABOUT THIS MEDIEVAL SPANISH HERO	**$600**	WHO IS
SHAKESPEAREAN WOMAN WHO ASKS, "WHERE IS THE BEAU-TEOUS MAJESTY OF DENMARK?"	**$800**	WHO IS
THE WORKS OF THIS 17th C. FRENCHMAN, INCLUDING "ANDRO-MACHE" & "PHAEDRA", ARE KNOWN FOR THEIR LACK OF ACTION	**$1000**	WHO IS

DOUBLE JEOPARDY!

CLASSIC DRAMA

$200	WHAT IS "HEDDA GABLER"?	**$200**
$400	WHO IS OEDIPUS?	**$400**
$600	WHO IS EL CID?	**$600**
$800	WHO IS OPHELIA?	**$800**
$1000	WHO IS JEAN RACINE?	**$1000**

DOUBLE JEOPARDY!

GOOD SPORTS

THIS BIG FELLA AVERAGED 55 HOME RUNS IN 1996 & 1997, BUT WAS JUST GETTING WARMED UP	$200	WHO IS
HE CONQUERED CANCER TO BECOME ONLY THE SECOND AMERICAN TO WIN THE TOUR DE FRANCE	$400	WHO IS
HIS 1990 KNOCKOUT OF MIKE TYSON HAS BEEN CALLED THE GREATEST HEAVY-WEIGHT TITLE UPSET	$600	WHO IS
THIS "GODDESS" BEAT LINDSAY DAVENPORT AT WIMBLEDON 2000 FOR HER FIRST GRAND SLAM SINGLES TITLE	$800	WHO IS
THIS VETERAN BOSTON DEFENSEMAN WENT TO COLORADO IN 2000 TO TRY TO WIN A STANLEY CUP	$1000	WHO IS

DOUBLE JEOPARDY!

GOOD SPORTS

$200	WHO IS MARK McGWIRE?	**$200**
$400	WHO IS LANCE ARMSTRONG?	**$400**
$600	WHO IS JAMES "BUSTER" DOUGLAS?	**$600**
$800	WHO IS VENUS WILLIAMS?	**$800**
$1000	WHO IS RAYMOND BOURQUE?	**$1000**

DOUBLE JEOPARDY!

WORLD HODGEPODGE

IN ITALY, A KINDLY WITCH CALLED BEFANA DELIVERS CHRISTMAS GIFTS, RIDING FROM HOUSE TO HOUSE ON ONE OF THESE	$200	WHAT IS
THE BHARATA NATYAM IS A HIGHLY STYLIZED DANCE THAT ORIGINATED IN THIS COUNTRY	$400	WHAT IS
AZERI IS THE OFFICIAL LANGUAGE OF THIS COUNTRY	$600	WHAT IS
ASSINIBOINE PARK IN THIS CAPITAL OF MANITOBA BOASTS A MINIATURE RAILWAY	$800	WHAT IS
MISS UNIVERSE 1992, MICHELLE McLEAN, FOUNDED A CHILDREN'S TRUST IN THIS COUNTRY ONCE KNOWN AS SOUTH WEST AFRICA	$1000	WHAT IS

DOUBLE JEOPARDY!

WORLD HODGEPODGE

$200 — WHAT IS A BROOMSTICK? — $200

$400 — WHAT IS INDIA? — $400

$600 — WHAT IS AZERBAIJAN? — $600

$800 — WHAT IS WINNEPEG? — $800

$1000 — WHAT IS NAMIBIA? — $1000

DOUBLE JEOPARDY!

U.S. U.N. REPS

5 YEARS AFTER EISEN-HOWER DEFEATED HIM A SECOND TIME, HE PACKED HIS BAGS & HEADED TO THE U.N.	**$200**	WHO IS
HE WENT FROM THE U.N. IN 1976 TO THE U.S. SENATE REPRE-SENTING NEW YORK IN 1977	**$400**	WHO IS
THIS MAN FROM NEW MEXICO WENT FROM THE U.N. TO THE POST OF SECRETARY OF ENERGY UNDER CLINTON	**$600**	WHO IS
IN 1981 SHE BECAME THE FIRST WOMAN THE U.S. PUT INTO THE POST	**$800**	WHO IS
IN 1960 HE WAS A U.N. AMBASSADOR & NIXON'S RUNNING MATE	**$1000**	WHO IS

DOUBLE JEOPARDY!

U.S. U.N. REPS

$200	WHO IS ADLAI STEVENSON?	**$200**
$400	WHO IS DANIEL PATRICK MOYNIHAN?	**$400**
$600	WHO IS BILL RICHARDSON?	**$600**
$800	WHO IS JEANE J. KIRKPATRICK?	**$800**
$1000	WHO IS HENRY CABOT LODGE, JR.?	**$1000**

DOUBLE JEOPARDY!

ENDS IN "LE"

TO LOSE CONTROL OF THE PIGSKIN	**$200**	WHAT IS
PROVERBIALLY, TO DALLY IN THE FACE OF A CRISIS IS TO DO THIS "WHILE ROME BURNS"	**$400**	WHAT IS
IF YOU'RE GONNA SET ON THE PORCH FOR A SPELL, YOU'LL WANT TO DO THIS TO SHAPE PIECES OF WOOD	**$600**	WHAT IS
SOME BIRDS ARE NAMED FOR THE ABILITY TO DO THIS, SING WITH TRILLS & QUAVERS	**$800**	WHAT IS
FROM OLD ENGLISH FOR "DART", IT MEANS TO MOVE BACK & FORTH BETWEEN 2 PLACES—PERHAPS EARTH & SPACE	**$1000**	WHAT IS

DOUBLE JEOPARDY!

ENDS IN "LE"

$200	WHAT IS FUMBLE?	**$200**
$400	WHAT IS FIDDLE?	**$400**
$600	WHAT IS WHITTLE?	**$600**
$800	WHAT IS WARBLE?	**$800**
$1000	WHAT IS SHUTTLE?	**$1000**

FINAL JEOPARDY!

FAMOUS FATHERS

HE PLAYED RHYTHM &
BLUES GUITAR BEFORE
WORKING AS A CRANE
OPERATOR & RAISING A
FAMILY IN GARY, INDIANA

WHO IS

FINAL JEOPARDY!

FAMOUS FATHERS

WHO IS JOSEPH JACKSON?

JEOPARDY!

THE BAD OLD DAYS

IT WASN'T A COLLEGE FOOTBALL GAME, IT WAS THE GREAT PLAINS AREA RACKED BY DROUGHT IN THE 1930s	**$100**	WHAT IS
1950s COLLEGE BASKETBALL WAS HIT BY SCANDAL WHEN PLAYERS WERE "RAZOR"-SHARP AT THIS ACTIVITY	**$200**	WHAT IS
THE SCANDALS OF HIS 1920s PRESIDENCY INCLUDED SKIMMING BY VETERANS BUREAU HEAD CHARLES FORBES	**$300**	WHO IS
THE FOUNDING OF THIS ORGANIZATION IN 1909 WAS SPURRED BY A SPRINGFIELD, ILL. RACE RIOT THE PREVIOUS YEAR	**$400**	WHAT IS
ORIGINALLY MEANING "FOREIGNERS", IT REFERS TO THOSE WHO OVERRAN THE ROMAN EMPIRE & BEGAN THE DARK AGES	**$500**	WHO ARE

JEOPARDY!

THE BAD OLD DAYS

$100	WHAT IS THE DUST BOWL?	**$100**
$200	WHAT IS POINT SHAVING?	**$200**
$300	WHO IS WARREN G. HARDING?	**$300**
$400	WHAT IS THE NAACP?	**$400**
$500	WHO ARE BARBARIANS?	**$500**

JEOPARDY!

ENDS IN "ELLA"

Clue	Value	Response
CHEESE FOR PIZZA	$100	WHAT IS
CHARLES PERRAULT'S VERSION ADDED THE GLASS SLIPPER TO HER STORY	$200	WHO IS
NAME SHOUTED IN THE CONCLUSION OF THE FILM "A STREETCAR NAMED DESIRE"	$300	WHAT IS
BACTERIA OFTEN FOUND IN CONTAM-INATED FOOD, NOT JUST CERTAIN FISH	$400	WHAT IS
ACTRESS SCIORRA	$500	WHO IS

JEOPARDY!

ENDS IN "ELLA"

$100	WHAT IS MOZZARELLA?	**$100**
$200	WHO IS CINDERELLA?	**$200**
$300	WHAT IS "STELLA"?	**$300**
$400	WHAT IS SALMONELLA?	**$400**
$500	WHO IS ANNABELLA?	**$500**

JEOPARDY!

STATE CAPITALS

MUSICALLY, THIS CAPITAL IS KNOWN FOR ITS "POPS" CONCERTS & SUMMER CONCERTS ON THE CHARLES RIVER ESPLANADE	**$100**	WHAT IS
THIS SMALL CAPITAL LIES AT THE WESTERN EDGE OF ITS STATE'S BLUEGRASS REGION	**$200**	WHAT IS
IT WAS THE ORIGINAL WESTERN TERMINUS OF THE TRANSCONTINENTAL RAILROAD	**$300**	WHAT IS
A STATUE OF ETHAN ALLEN GRACES THE CAPITOL BUILDING PORTICO IN THIS CITY	**$400**	WHAT IS
THIS CAPITAL'S EXECUTIVE MANSION WAS ONCE THE HOME OF JAMES G. BLAINE	**$500**	WHAT IS

JEOPARDY!

STATE CAPITALS

$100	WHAT IS BOSTON?	**$100**
$200	WHAT IS FRANKFORT?	**$200**
$300	WHAT IS SACRAMENTO?	**$300**
$400	WHAT IS MONTPELIER?	**$400**
$500	WHAT IS AUGUSTA?	**$500**

JEOPARDY!™

FOOD STUFF

IT'S NO FISH STORY: CIOPPINO IS A FISH STEW FROM THIS CITY'S FISHERMAN'S WHARF	**$100**	WHAT IS
THIS CUT OF BEEF THAT'S ALSO A MAN'S NICKNAME COMES FROM BETWEEN THE NECK & THE SHOULDER BLADE	**$200**	WHAT IS
BEURRE BERCY IS MADE WITH WHITE WINE, SHALLOTS, DICED BEEF MARROW, PARSLEY, & OF COURSE, THIS SPREAD	**$300**	WHAT IS
THIS TART, YELLOWISH LIME THAT'S NATIVE TO FLORIDA IS THE MAIN INGREDIENT IN A POPULAR PIE	**$400**	WHAT IS
IN SCOTLAND THESE "COLORFUL" BERRIES ARE CALLED BRAMBLES, & SCOTS MAKE BRAMBLE WINE FROM THEM	**$500**	WHAT ARE

JEOPARDY!

FOOD STUFF

$100   WHAT IS SAN FRANCISCO? $100

$200   WHAT IS CHUCK? $200

$300   WHAT IS BUTTER? $300

$400   WHAT IS KEY LIME? $400

$500   WHAT ARE BLACKBERRIES? $500

JEOPARDY!

SPORTS MEDICINE

THE "STRESS" TYPE IS A HAIRLINE BREAK CAUSED BY OVERUSE	**$100**	WHAT IS
IN TENDINITIS & BURSITIS, -ITIS DENOTES THIS	**$200**	WHAT IS
A TEAR TO THE ACL, OR ANTERIOR CRUCIATE ONE OF THESE IN THE KNEE, HAS BROUGHT MANY ATHLETES TO THEIR KNEES	**$300**	WHAT IS
THEY'RE THE MUSCLES THAT FLEX THE KNEE: PIGS PROBABLY DON'T INJURE THEIRS AS OFTEN AS HUMANS DO	**$400**	WHAT ARE
TO PRO ATHLETES, A "SCOPE" IS USUALLY SHORT FOR THIS TYPE OF DEVICE TO VIEW THE INTERIOR OF A JOINT CAVITY	**$500**	WHAT IS

JEOPARDY!

SPORTS MEDICINE

$100	WHAT IS A FRACTURE?	**$100**
$200	WHAT IS INFLAMMATION?	**$200**
$300	WHAT IS LIGAMENT?	**$300**
$400	WHAT ARE HAMSTRINGS?	**$400**
$500	WHAT IS ARTHROSCOPE?	**$500**

JEOPARDY!

NEWSMEN/AUTHORS

IN 1997's "A REPORTER'S LIFE" HE COVERED HIS 31 YEARS AT CBS NEWS	**$100**	WHO IS
THIS NBC ANCHOR'S "THE GREATEST GENERATION" PAID TRIBUTE TO THOSE WHO CAME OF AGE DURING WORLD WAR II	**$200**	WHO IS
IN 1998 THIS ABC ANCHOR, ALONG WITH TODD BREWSTER, TOOK ON "THE CENTURY"	**$300**	WHO IS
HE & KYLE GIBSON WROTE "NIGHTLINE: HISTORY IN THE MAKING AND THE MAKING OF TELEVISION"	**$400**	WHO IS
"EVERYONE IS ENTITLED TO MY OPINION" COLLECTED HIS COMMENTARIES FROM "THIS WEEK"	**$500**	WHO IS

JEOPARDY!

NEWSMEN/AUTHORS

$100 — WHO IS WALTER CRONKITE? — $100

$200 — WHO IS TOM BROKAW? — $200

$300 — WHO IS PETER JENNINGS? — $300

$400 — WHO IS TED KOPPEL? — $400

$500 — WHO IS DAVID BRINKLEY? — $500

DOUBLE JEOPARDY!

LITERARY OPENINGS

THIS SEUSS TALE BEGINS, "EVERY WHO DOWN IN WHO-VILLE LIKED CHRISTMAS A LOT . . ."	**$200**	WHAT IS
THE STORY OF THIS UNHAPPY RUSSIAN WOMAN BEGINS WITH A FAMOUS REMARK ABOUT HAPPY & UNHAPPY FAMILIES	**$400**	WHO IS
HIS "THE MALTESE FALCON" OPENS "SAMUEL SPADE'S JAW WAS LONG AND BONY"	**$600**	WHO IS
"IT WAS A PLEASURE TO BURN" BEGINS THIS RAY BRADBURY BOOK WITH A TEMPERATURE FOR ITS TITLE	**$800**	WHAT IS
THIS FRENCH AUTHOR'S "THE STRANGER" LACONICALLY BEGINS, "MY MOTHER DIED. TODAY, OR MAYBE IT WAS YESTERDAY."	**$1000**	WHO IS

DOUBLE JEOPARDY!

LITERARY OPENINGS

$200	WHAT IS "HOW THE GRINCH STOLE CHRISTMAS"?	**$200**
$400	WHO IS ANNA KARENINA?	**$400**
$600	WHO IS DASHIELL HAMMETT?	**$600**
$800	WHAT IS "FAHRENHEIT 451"?	**$800**
$1000	WHO IS ALBERT CAMUS?	**$1000**

DOUBLE JEOPARDY!

COLLEGE TEAM NICKNAMES

DIFFERENT CAMPUSES OF THE UNIVERSITY OF THIS STATE ARE HOME TO ANTEATERS, BANANA SLUGS & GOLDEN BEARS	**$200**	WHAT IS
THIS WORD PRECEDES THE IRISH OF NOTRE DAME & THE ILLINI OF THE UNIVERSITY OF ILLINOIS	**$400**	WHAT IS
THIS CANINE REPRESENTS OVER 30 COLLEGES IN-CLUDING YALE & THE UNIVERSITY OF GEORGIA	**$600**	WHAT IS
THE MEN'S TEAMS AT NORTHLAND COLLEGE IN WISCON-SIN ARE THE LUMBER-JACKS & THE WOMEN'S TEAMS ARE THESE	**$800**	WHO ARE
OHIO STATE HONORS EACH OF ITS ALL-AMERICANS BY PLANT-ING ONE OF THESE MASCOT TREES IN A GROVE	**$1000**	WHAT ARE

DOUBLE JEOPARDY!

COLLEGE TEAM NICKNAMES

$200 WHAT IS CALIFORNIA? **$200**

$400 WHAT IS FIGHTING? **$400**

$600 WHAT IS THE BULLDOG? **$600**

$800 WHO ARE THE LUMBERJILLS? **$800**

$1000 WHAT ARE BUCKEYES? **$1000**

DOUBLE JEOPARDY!

IT'S JAPANESE TO ME

JAPAN'S CURRENCY IS CALLED THIS, MEANING "ROUND", AS OPPOSED TO EARLIER COINS, WHICH WERE OFTEN SQUARE	**$200**	WHAT IS
"ARIGATO" IS JAPANESE FOR THIS & "DOMO ARIGATO GOZAI-MASHTA" IS JAPANESE FOR THIS "VERY MUCH"	**$400**	WHAT IS
THE GREEN TYPE OF THIS BEVERAGE IS CALLED AGARI, "FINISHED"	**$600**	WHAT IS
THESE FEMALE ENTERTAINERS ARE FOUND IN THE KARYUKAI, "FLOWER & WILLOW WORLD"	**$800**	WHAT ARE
WHEN YOU TRY TO CATCH THESE CULTIVATED CARP, YOU'D EXPECT THEM TO PLAY HARD TO GET	**$1000**	WHAT ARE

DOUBLE JEOPARDY!

IT'S JAPANESE TO ME

$200 — WHAT IS THE YEN? — $200

$400 — WHAT IS THANK YOU? — $400

$600 — WHAT IS TEA? — $600

$800 — WHAT ARE GEISHA? — $800

$1000 — WHAT ARE KOI? — $1000

DOUBLE JEOPARDY!

TV MINISERIES

YOU COULD CALL HENRY THOMAS ISHMAEL & PATRICK STEWART AHAB IN THIS 1998 MINISERIES	**$200**	WHAT IS
VANESSA WILLIAMS PLAYED CALYPSO & GRETA SCACCHI WAS THE LONG-SUFFERING PENELOPE IN THIS 1997 EPIC	**$400**	WHAT IS
THE 2000 MINISERIES ABOUT THIS "KING-DOM" FEATURED CAMRYN MANHEIM AS SNOW WHITE	**$600**	WHAT IS
ROBERT DUVALL SAT TALL IN THE SADDLE AS AUGUSTUS McCRAE IN THIS 1989 4-PART WESTERN	**$800**	WHAT IS
IN 1994 STEPHEN COLLINS PLAYED ASHLEY WILKES IN THIS MINISERIES SEQUEL TO "GONE WITH THE WIND"	**$1000**	WHAT IS

DOUBLE JEOPARDY!

TV MINISERIES

$200 WHAT IS "MOBY DICK"? **$200**

$400 WHAT IS "THE ODYSSEY"? **$400**

$600 WHAT IS "THE 10th KINGDOM"? **$600**

$800 WHAT IS "LONESOME DOVE"? **$800**

$1000 WHAT IS "SCARLETT"? **$1000**

DOUBLE JEOPARDY!

PHARAOHS

Clue	Value	Response
LORD CARNARVON REPORTEDLY CALLED THIS RULER'S TOMB "THE GREATEST SIGHT I HAVE EVER WITNESSED"	$200	WHO IS
WHILE ONLY A PRINCE, TUTHMOSIS IV HAD THIS COLOSSAL STATUE OF GIZA RESTORED	$400	WHAT IS
THIS ANCIENT CAPITAL GREW UP AROUND PEPI I's PYRAMID, MEN-NEFER-MARE	$600	WHAT IS
2-WORD NAME FOR THE SITE SOUTH OF CAIRO WHERE RAMSES II BUILT 2 SANDSTONE TEMPLES	$800	WHAT IS
NAME SHARED BY THE SECOND KING OF THE 19th DYNASTY & THE SEARCH FOR EXTRATERRESTRIAL INTELLIGENCE	$1000	WHAT IS

DOUBLE JEOPARDY!

PHARAOHS

$200	WHO IS KING TUT?	**$200**
$400	WHAT IS THE (GREAT) SPHINX?	**$400**
$600	WHAT IS MEMPHIS?	**$600**
$800	WHAT IS ABU SIMBEL?	**$800**
$1000	WHAT IS SETI?	**$1000**

DOUBLE JEOPARDY!

NEW YORK BUILDINGS

ITS ARCHITECT, WILLIAM VAN ALEN, WAS "DRIVEN" TO CREATE THE WORLD'S TALLEST BUILDING AT THAT TIME	**$200**	WHAT IS
THIS BUILDING, JOHN LENNON'S LAST RESIDENCE, WAS SO NAMED BECAUSE 72nd ST. SEEMED LIKE THE FAR WEST	**$400**	WHAT IS
THE OLD RCA BUILDING AT 30 ROCKEFELLER PLAZA IS NOW CALLED THIS "BUILDING", ONE INITIAL SHORTER	**$600**	WHAT IS
THE BUILDING NAMED FOR THIS RETAILER INCLUDES A SCULPTURE OF HIM COUNTING NICKELS & DIMES	**$800**	WHO IS
NAMED FOR ITS DEVELOPER, THIS MIDTOWN TOWER HAS AN ATRIUM WITH A WATERFALL INSTEAD OF A MERE LOBBY	**$1000**	WHAT IS

DOUBLE JEOPARDY!

NEW YORK BUILDINGS

$200	WHAT IS THE CHRYSLER BUILDING?	$200
$400	WHAT IS THE DAKOTA?	$400
$600	WHAT IS THE GE BUILDING?	$600
$800	WHO IS F. W. WOOLWORTH?	$800
$1000	WHAT IS TRUMP TOWER?	$1000

FINAL JEOPARDY!

SONGWRITERS

IT WAS ONCE SAID OF THIS
MAN WHO LIVED TO BE 101:
HE "HAS NO PLACE IN
AMERICAN MUSIC. HE IS
AMERICAN MUSIC"

WHO IS

FINAL JEOPARDY!

SONGWRITERS

WHO IS IRVING BERLIN?

JEOPARDY!™

FAMOUS WOMEN

NICKNAME OF AL GORE'S WIFE MARY ELIZABETH	**$100**	WHAT IS
CINDY CRAWFORD IS ONE OF "THE MOST UNFORGETTABLE WOMEN IN THE WORLD" WHO WEAR THIS MAKEUP BRAND	**$200**	WHAT IS
IN 1998 TARA LIPINSKI REPLACED THIS NORWEGIAN LASS AS THE YOUNGEST OLYMPIC FIGURE SKATING CHAMP	**$300**	WHO IS
ONCE A MEMBER OF THE "BRAT PACK", SHE RETURNED TO THE BIG SCREEN AS A PHOTOG-RAPHER IN 1998's "HIGH ART"	**$400**	WHO IS
THIS UNFORTUNATELY NAMED WOMAN WHO FOUNDED THE HOUSTON SYMPHONY NEVER HAD A SISTER NAMED URA HOGG	**$500**	WHO IS

JEOPARDY!

FAMOUS WOMEN

$100	WHAT IS TIPPER?	**$100**
$200	WHAT IS REVLON?	**$200**
$300	WHO IS SONJA HENIE?	**$300**
$400	WHO IS ALLY SHEEDY?	**$400**
$500	WHO IS IMA HOGG?	**$500**

JEOPARDY!™

THE NORMANS

THE NORMANS CALLED THEIR KNIGHTS THIS; ONE MAY HAVE BEEN MAURICE'S ANCESTOR	**$100**	WHAT ARE
IT TAKES A FIEF TO RUN THIS SYSTEM THAT THE NORMANS LEARNED FROM THE CAROLINGIANS	**$200**	WHAT IS
THIS BATTLE OF OCTOBER 14, 1066 ESTABLISHED THE NORMANS AS RULERS OF ENGLAND	**$300**	WHAT IS
NORMAN CRUSADER TANCRED OF HAUTE-VILLE BECAME PRINCE OF THIS REGION OF PALESTINE KNOWN FOR ITS SEA	**$400**	WHAT IS
THE FIRST NORMAN FOOTHOLD IN FRANCE WAS NEAR THIS CITY WHERE JOAN OF ARC MET HER END	**$500**	WHAT IS

JEOPARDY!

THE NORMANS

$100   WHAT ARE CHEVALIERS?   **$100**

$200   WHAT IS THE FEUDAL SYSTEM?   **$200**

$300   WHAT IS THE BATTLE OF HASTINGS?   **$300**

$400   WHAT IS GALILEE?   **$400**

$500   WHAT IS ROUEN?   **$500**

JEOPARDY!

NATIONAL AIRLINES

ACCORDING TO "RAIN MAN", THIS AUSSIE AIRLINE IS THE ONLY ONE THAT NEVER CRASHED	**$100**	WHAT IS
YOU'LL FEEL LIKE A GOD ON OLYMPIC AIRWAYS, THIS COUNTRY'S NATIONAL AIRLINE	**$200**	WHAT IS
ALL FOOD IS STRICTLY KOSHER ON THIS NATIONAL AIRLINE ESTABLISHED IN 1949	**$300**	WHAT IS
LUXAIR AIRLINES IS THE NATIONAL CARRIER OF THIS GRAND DUCHY	**$400**	WHAT IS
ENGLISH INITIALS OF THE NATIONAL AIRLINE OF THE NETHERLANDS	**$500**	WHAT IS

JEOPARDY!

NATIONAL AIRLINES

$100   WHAT IS QANTAS? $100

$200   WHAT IS GREECE? $200

$300   WHAT IS EL AL? $300

$400   WHAT IS LUXEMBOURG? $400

$500   WHAT IS KLM? $500

JEOPARDY!

CROSSWORD CLUES "T"

DOROTHY'S DOGGIE (4)	**$100**	WHO IS
SURF'S PARTNER, ON A MENU (4)	**$200**	WHAT IS
BOW, OR BOLO (3)	**$300**	WHAT IS
SALTWATER SWEET (5)	**$400**	WHAT IS
HITCHHIKING ESSENTIAL (5)	**$500**	WHAT IS

JEOPARDY!

CROSSWORD CLUES "T"

$100	WHO IS TOTO?	$100
$200	WHAT IS TURF?	$200
$300	WHAT IS A TIE?	$300
$400	WHAT IS TAFFY?	$400
$500	WHAT IS A THUMB?	$500

JEOPARDY!™

U.S. BODIES OF WATER

THE CHICAGO RIVER ORIGINALLY FLOWED INTO THIS GREAT LAKE; NOW IT FLOWS OUT OF IT	$100	WHAT IS
BRINE FLIES & BRINE SHRIMP ARE THE ONLY CREATURES THAT THRIVE IN THIS BODY OF WATER NEAR UTAH'S CAPITAL	$200	WHAT IS
YOU'LL FIND THE BIG BRANCH NATIONAL WILDLIFE REFUGE ON THE SHORE OF THIS BIG LAKE IN LOUISIANA	$300	WHAT IS
THERE'S A COEUR D'ALENE LAKE & A COEUR D'ALENE RIVER IN THIS STATE	$400	WHAT IS
WE HOPE YOU KNOW THAT MOUNT HOPE BAY IN RHODE ISLAND IS AN ARM OF THIS LARGER BAY	$500	WHAT IS

JEOPARDY!

U.S. BODIES OF WATER

$100	WHAT IS LAKE MICHIGAN?	$100
$200	WHAT IS THE GREAT SALT LAKE?	$200
$300	WHAT IS LAKE PONTCHARTRAIN?	$300
$400	WHAT IS IDAHO?	$400
$500	WHAT IS NARRAGANSETT BAY?	$500

JEOPARDY!™

TRUSTY SIDEKICKS

COMIC BOOK SIDEKICK KNOWN AS THE "BOY WONDER"	**$100**	WHO IS
HE NAVIGATED THE JUNGLE WITH THE AID OF CHEETAH, A CHIMP	**$200**	WHO IS
HE'S PENN'S SILENT SIDEKICK	**$300**	WHO IS
PROFESSION OF SHERLOCK HOLMES' FAITHFUL WATSON	**$400**	WHAT IS
IN 2000 THIS TRUSTY LATE-NIGHT SIDEKICK LEFT CONAN O'BRIEN'S SIDE	**$500**	WHO IS

JEOPARDY!

TRUSTY SIDEKICKS

$100	WHO IS ROBIN?	$100
$200	WHO IS TARZAN?	$200
$300	WHO IS TELLER?	$300
$400	WHAT IS DOCTOR?	$400
$500	WHO IS ANDY RICHTER?	$500

DOUBLE JEOPARDY!

FRUIT

Clue	Value	Response
THE BING & OTHER SWEET VARIETIES OF THIS FRUIT ARE SELF-STERILE; THEY CANNOT POLLINATE THEMSELVES	**$200**	WHAT IS
THE BARTLETT TYPE OF THIS FRUIT BEGINS TO RIPEN IN SUMMER; OTHER VARIETIES RIPEN LATER IN THE YEAR	**$400**	WHAT IS
THIS FRUIT OFTEN ORIGINATES FROM PEACH SEEDS & PEACHES SOMETIMES COME FROM ITS SEEDS	**$600**	WHAT IS
A CLUSTER, OR HAND, OF THIS FRUIT CONSISTS OF 10–20 FINGERS	**$800**	WHAT IS
THIS HYBRID OF A TANGERINE & A GRAPEFRUIT COMES IN 2 MAIN VARIETIES: ORLANDO & MINNEOLA	**$1000**	WHAT IS

DOUBLE JEOPARDY!

FRUIT

$200	WHAT IS THE CHERRY?	**$200**
$400	WHAT IS THE PEAR?	**$400**
$600	WHAT IS THE NECTARINE?	**$600**
$800	WHAT IS THE BANANA?	**$800**
$1000	WHAT IS THE TANGELO?	**$1000**

DOUBLE JEOPARDY!

THE ARTICLES OF CONFEDERATION

THE ARTICLES WERE IN EFFECT FROM 1781 UNTIL REPLACED BY THIS 1787 DOCUMENT	**$200**	WHAT IS
RICHARD HENRY LEE PROPOSED DRAFTING THE ARTICLES ON JUNE 7 OF THIS YEAR	**$400**	WHAT IS
UNDER ARTICLE XI THIS PRESENT-DAY COUNTRY COULD HAVE JOINED THE CONFEDERATION JUST BY SIGNING	**$600**	WHAT IS
THE ARTICLES' LACK OF NATIONAL TAXATION IS CRITICIZED IN NO. 21 OF THESE ESSAYS	**$800**	WHAT IS
THE "REBELLION" HE LED IN 1786 SHOWED MANY THAT THE ARTICLES DIDN'T INCLUDE A STRONG ENOUGH CENTRAL GOVERNMENT	**$1000**	WHO IS

DOUBLE JEOPARDY!

THE ARTICLES OF CONFEDERATION

$200 — WHAT IS THE CONSTITUTION? — $200

$400 — WHAT IS 1776? — $400

$600 — WHAT IS CANADA? — $600

$800 — WHAT IS "THE FEDERALIST" (PAPERS)? — $800

$1000 — WHO IS DANIEL SHAYS? — $1000

DOUBLE JEOPARDY!

MOVIES ABOUT THE MOVIES

THIS GENE KELLY MUSICAL TAKES PLACE IN A HOLLYWOOD MAKING THE ADJUSTMENT TO TALKIES	**$200**	WHAT IS
HE DIRECTED "8½", A MOVIE ABOUT A MOVIE DIRECTOR	**$400**	WHO IS
IN THIS 1941 PRESTON STURGES FILM, A DIRECTOR SETS OUT TO RESEARCH POVERTY WITH ONLY A DIME IN HIS POCKET	**$600**	WHAT IS
JOHN TURTURRO PLAYED THIS TITLE SCREENWRITER IN A 1991 COEN BROTHERS FILM	**$800**	WHO IS
THE 1998 FILM "GODS AND MONSTERS" PRESENTS THE LAST DAYS OF THIS DIRECTOR OF "FRANKENSTEIN"	**$1000**	WHO IS

DOUBLE JEOPARDY!

MOVIES ABOUT THE MOVIES

$200   WHAT IS "SINGIN' IN THE RAIN"? $200

$400   WHO IS FEDERICO FELLINI? $400

$600   WHAT IS "SULLIVAN'S TRAVELS"? $600

$800   WHO IS BARTON FINK? $800

$1000   WHO IS JAMES WHALE? $1000

DOUBLE JEOPARDY!

THAT'S WHAT THEY SAID

AFTER HER ELECTION, THIS BRITISH PRIME MINISTER SAID THAT SHE OWED "EVERYTHING TO MY FATHER"	**$200**	WHO IS
THIS AUTHOR'S MR. BUMBLE DECLARED THAT "THE LAW IS A ASS, A IDIOT"	**$400**	WHO IS
IN 1803 JACQUES DELILLE WROTE, "FATE CHOOSES OUR RELATIVES, WE CHOOSE" THESE	**$600**	WHAT ARE
"WHEN THE ONE GREAT SCORER COMES TO WRITE AGAINST YOUR NAME, HE MARKS—NOT THAT YOU WON OR LOST—BUT" THIS	**$800**	WHAT IS
IN HIS 1918 POEM "PRAIRIE", HE WROTE "I TELL YOU THE PAST IS A BUCKET OF ASHES"	**$1000**	WHO IS

DOUBLE JEOPARDY!

THAT'S WHAT THEY SAID

$200	WHO IS MARGARET THATCHER?	**$200**
$400	WHO IS CHARLES DICKENS?	**$400**
$600	WHAT ARE "OUR FRIENDS"?	**$600**
$800	WHAT IS "HOW YOU PLAYED THE GAME"?	**$800**
$1000	WHO IS CARL SANDBURG?	**$1000**

DOUBLE JEOPARDY!

THE FATHERS OF ...

"THE FATHER OF FROZEN FOODS", HE BECAME A CONSULTANT TO GENERAL FOODS	**$200**	WHO IS
BEFORE HE WAS "THE FATHER OF BASKETBALL", HE WAS A STAR LACROSSE PLAYER	**$400**	WHO IS
WE'LL TAKE AN OATH THAT HE'S "THE FATHER OF MEDICINE"	**$600**	WHO IS
HE MADE LIFE MISERABLE FOR BOSS TWEED AS "THE FATHER OF AMERICAN POLITICAL CARTOONISTS"	**$800**	WHO IS
AS YOU MIGHT EXPECT, A MAN WITH THIS COMMON LAST NAME WAS "THE FATHER OF THE TOMMY GUN"	**$1000**	WHAT IS

DOUBLE JEOPARDY!

THE FATHERS OF ...

$200	WHO IS CLARENCE BIRDSEYE?	**$200**
$400	WHO IS JAMES NAISMITH?	**$400**
$600	WHO IS HIPPOCRATES?	**$600**
$800	WHO IS THOMAS NAST?	**$800**
$1000	WHAT IS THOMPSON?	**$1000**

DOUBLE JEOPARDY!

WORLD CAPITALS

WHEN IT GETS HOT IN THIS SOUTH AMERICAN COUNTRY, YOU MAY WANT TO DO THE FULL MONTEVIDEO	$200	WHAT IS
THE HEADQUARTERS OF THE ORGANIZATION OF AFRICAN UNITY ARE IN THIS ETHIOPIAN CAPITAL	$400	WHAT IS
THIS COUNTRY'S CAPITAL, VIENTIANE, IS LOCATED ON THE MEKONG RIVER	$600	WHAT IS
TIRANE, NOT TO BE CONFUSED WITH TEHRAN, IS THE CAPITAL OF THIS BALKAN NATION	$800	WHAT IS
IN MAY 2000 GEORGE SPEIGHT LED A COUP IN SUVA, THIS COUNTRY'S CAPITAL	$1000	WHAT IS

DOUBLE JEOPARDY!

WORLD CAPITALS

$200	WHAT IS URUGUAY?	**$200**
$400	WHAT IS ADDIS ABABA?	**$400**
$600	WHAT IS LAOS?	**$600**
$800	WHAT IS ALBANIA?	**$800**
$1000	WHAT IS FIJI?	**$1000**

154

BUSINESS MACHINES

THIS TYPE OF MACHINE, IN THE NEWS IN 1987, WAS DEVELOPED IN THE '70s FROM A NOODLE-MAKING DEVICE

WHAT IS

FINAL JEOPARDY!

BUSINESS MACHINES

WHAT IS A
(PAPER) SHREDDER?

JEOPARDY!

1820s AMERICA

ON OCT. 26, 1825 THE SENECA CHIEF LEFT BUFFALO & BECAME THE FIRST BOAT TO TRAVEL THIS WATER-WAY'S ENTIRE LENGTH	**$100**	WHAT IS
DISCOVERED IN 1806, THIS COLORADO PEAK WAS FIRST CLIMBED IN 1820 BY 3 MEMBERS OF MAJOR LONG'S EXPEDITION	**$200**	WHAT IS
ON JUNE 17, 1825 THIS FRENCHMAN LAID THE CORNERSTONE OF THE BUNKER HILL MONUMENT	**$300**	WHO IS
IN 1821 IT ENTERED THE UNION AS A SLAVE STATE WITH THOMAS HART BENTON REPRE-SENTING IT IN THE SENATE	**$400**	WHAT IS
IN HIS 1829 MESSAGE TO CONGRESS, ANDREW JACKSON QUESTIONED THE CONSTITUTIONALITY OF THIS INSTITUTION	**$500**	WHAT IS

JEOPARDY!

1820s AMERICA

$100 | WHAT IS THE ERIE CANAL? | **$100**

$200 | WHAT IS PIKES PEAK? | **$200**

$300 | WHO IS THE MARQUIS DE LAFAYETTE? | **$300**

$400 | WHAT IS MISSOURI? | **$400**

$500 | WHAT IS THE BANK OF THE UNITED STATES? | **$500**

JEOPARDY!

"SMALL" TIME

IN 1979 THE WORLD HEALTH ORGANIZATION MARKED THE DISAPPEARANCE OF THIS VIRAL DISEASE FROM THE EARTH	$100	WHAT IS
THIS FEDERAL LOAN-ASSISTANCE AGENCY LOCATED IN WASHINGTON, D.C. IS KNOWN AS THE SBA FOR SHORT	$200	WHAT IS
IT'S WHAT YOU SAY ON FINDING OUT THAT A NEW ACQUAINTANCE WENT TO COLLEGE WITH YOUR UNCLE'S DOCTOR'S COUSIN	$300	WHAT IS
1998 FILM ABOUT TOY ACTION FIGURES TURNED MENACING	$400	WHAT IS
THE NATIONAL WEATHER SERVICE ISSUES SAILORS THESE "ADVISORIES" WHEN WINDS ARE BETWEEN 18 & 33 KNOTS	$500	WHAT IS

JEOPARDY!

"SMALL" TIME

$100	WHAT IS SMALLPOX?	**$100**
$200	WHAT IS THE SMALL BUSINESS ADMINISTRATION?	**$200**
$300	WHAT IS "SMALL WORLD!"?	**$300**
$400	WHAT IS "SMALL SOLDIERS"?	**$400**
$500	WHAT IS A SMALL CRAFT ADVISORY?	**$500**

160

JEOPARDY!

GANGSTERS

Clue	Value	Response
HE'S QUOTED AS SAYING, "THEY'VE HUNG EVERYTHING ON ME BUT THE CHICAGO FIRE"	**$100**	WHO IS
ARNOLD "THE BRAIN" ROTHSTEIN WAS AC-CUSED OF MASTER-MINDING THE BIG FIX OF THIS IN 1919; IT WASN'T PROVED	**$200**	WHAT IS
HIS BROTHER BUCK WAS PART OF HIS GANG, AS WAS HIS MOLL BONNIE	**$300**	WHO IS
HIS FATEFUL JULY 22, 1934 NIGHT AT CHICAGO'S BIOGRAPH THEATER MIGHT BE FEATURED ON "BIOGRAPHY"	**$400**	WHO IS
BRIBES FROM BIG BILL DWYER TURNED MEMBERS OF THIS ARMED SERVICE INTO RUM-RUNNERS	**$500**	WHO ARE

JEOPARDY!

GANGSTERS

$100	WHO IS AL CAPONE?	**$100**
$200	WHAT IS THE WORLD SERIES?	**$200**
$300	WHO IS CLYDE BARROW?	**$300**
$400	WHO IS JOHN DILLINGER?	**$400**
$500	WHO ARE THE U.S. COAST GUARD?	**$500**

JEOPARDY!

1990s NONFICTION

Clue	Value	Response
NOTABLE ONES INCLUDE McCULLOUGH'S OF TRUMAN, BERG'S OF LINDBERGH & JACK MILES' OF GOD	$100	WHAT ARE
THIS NEWS PERSONALITY'S "AMERICA" TOLD OF HIS 12 FAVORITE PLACES FOUND "ON THE ROAD"	$200	WHO IS
SEYMOUR HERSH'S 1997 JFK EXPOSE WAS TITLED "THE DARK SIDE OF" THIS	$300	WHAT IS
THIS AUTHOR WAS BORN IN BROOKLYN BUT, AS "ANGELA'S ASHES" TELLS, GREW UP IN IRELAND	$400	WHO IS
A MOSCOW MAUSOLEUM, OR THE TITLE OF DAVID REMNICK'S BOOK ON "THE LAST DAYS OF THE SOVIET EMPIRE"	$500	WHAT IS

JEOPARDY!

1990s NONFICTION

$100	WHAT ARE BIOGRAPHIES?	**$100**
$200	WHO IS CHARLES KURALT?	**$200**
$300	WHAT IS "CAMELOT"?	**$300**
$400	WHO IS FRANK McCOURT?	**$400**
$500	WHAT IS LENIN'S TOMB?	**$500**

JEOPARDY!

BOXING TERMS

NEW TO THE SPORT? LET ME SHOW YOU THESE; THEY'RE STRUNG AROUND THE RING	**$100**	WHAT ARE
A PUNCH DELIVERED "BELOW" IT IS A FOUL (& MAY CAUSE YOU TO LOSE IT)	**$200**	WHAT IS
THE MOST IMPORTANT BOUT ON THE CARD; BARBRA STREISAND SANG ABOUT ONE	**$300**	WHAT IS
FOR THE COUNT, THE STANDING BOXER MUST RETIRE TO ONE OF THESE	**$400**	WHAT IS
IN 1982 NEVADA MADE THIS COUNT MANDATORY IN CASE OF A KNOCKDOWN	**$500**	WHAT IS

JEOPARDY!

BOXING TERMS

$100	WHAT ARE THE ROPES?	**$100**
$200	WHAT IS THE BELT?	**$200**
$300	WHAT IS "THE MAIN EVENT"?	**$300**
$400	WHAT IS A NEUTRAL CORNER?	**$400**
$500	WHAT IS AN (STANDING) EIGHT COUNT?	**$500**

JEOPARDY!

CHARLES DARWIN

CHARLES & THIS AMERICAN PRESIDENT WERE BORN ON THE SAME DAY, FEBRUARY 12, 1809; CHARLES LIVED MUCH LONGER	**$100**	WHO IS
YOUNG CHARLES HAD JOHN EDMONSTONE TEACH HIM THIS ART WHOSE MOTTO MAY BE "GET STUFFED"	**$200**	WHAT IS
IT WAS DARWIN'S FAVORITE PROFESSOR WHO RECOMMENDED HIM FOR THE NATURALIST POST ABOARD THIS SHIP	**$300**	WHAT IS
A GALAPAGOS GOVERNOR TOLD DARWIN HE COULD LOOK AT ONE OF THESE GIANT CREATURES & IDENTIFY ITS ISLAND	**$400**	WHAT ARE
THE GRANDFATHER OF THIS "BRAVE NEW WORLD" AUTHOR WAS KNOWN AS "DARWIN'S BULLDOG"	**$500**	WHO IS

JEOPARDY!™

CHARLES DARWIN

$100	WHO IS ABRAHAM LINCOLN?	**$100**
$200	WHAT IS TAXIDERMY?	**$200**
$300	WHAT IS THE BEAGLE?	**$300**
$400	WHAT ARE TORTOISES?	**$400**
$500	WHO IS ALDOUS HUXLEY?	**$500**

DOUBLE JEOPARDY!

MEET THE FLINTSTONES

"THE FLINTSTONES" WAS MODELED ON THIS JACKIE GLEASON SERIES	**$200**	WHAT IS
IN THE 1993 PRIME-TIME SPECIAL "I YABBA-DABBA DO!", THESE 2 KIDS GOT MARRIED	**$400**	WHO ARE
IN 1996, AFTER YEARS OF EXCLUSION & A NATIONAL VOTE, SHE JOINED THE REST OF THE GANG AS A FLINTSTONE VITAMIN	**$600**	WHO IS
KRISTEN JOHNSTON PLAYED WILMA IN THE 2000 FILM "THE FLINT-STONES IN VIVA" THIS PLACE	**$800**	WHAT IS
"THE FLINTSTONES" THEME IS BASED ON THE CHORD CHANGES OF THIS SONG; "WHO COULD ASK FOR ANYTHING MORE?"	**$1000**	WHAT IS

DOUBLE JEOPARDY!

MEET THE FLINTSTONES

$200	WHAT IS "THE HONEYMOONERS"?	$200
$400	WHO ARE PEBBLES & BAMM-BAMM?	$400
$600	WHO IS BETTY (RUBBLE)?	$600
$800	WHAT IS ROCK VEGAS?	$800
$1000	WHAT IS "I GOT RHYTHM"?	$1000

DOUBLE JEOPARDY!

GEOGRAPHY

MANY RESIDENTS OF THIS SPRAWLING VALLEY THAT INCLUDES NORTH HOLLYWOOD WANT TO SECEDE FROM LOS ANGELES	**$200**	WHAT IS
MOST OF THE RESIDENTS OF THIS SMALL ISLAND CITY-STATE OFF THE MALAY PENINSULA ARE CHINESE	**$400**	WHAT IS
THE SHRINE OF FATIMA IS IN THIS COUNTRY'S CITY OF QOM, NOT FAR FROM TEHRAN	**$600**	WHAT IS
QUEENSLAND & VICTORIA ARE 2 OF THIS COUNTRY'S STATES	**$800**	WHAT IS
THIS "STAN" IS WEDGED IN AMONG TURKMEN-ISTAN, KAZAKHSTAN, TAJIKISTAN & KYRGYZSTAN	**$1000**	WHAT IS

DOUBLE JEOPARDY!

GEOGRAPHY

$200 — WHAT IS THE SAN FERNANDO VALLEY? — **$200**

$400 — WHAT IS SINGAPORE? — **$400**

$600 — WHAT IS IRAN? — **$600**

$800 — WHAT IS AUSTRALIA? — **$800**

$1000 — WHAT IS UZBEKISTAN? — **$1000**

DOUBLE JEOPARDY!

GOING TO THE DOGE

NICKNAME OF THE BRIDGE ANTONIO CONTINO BUILT AROUND 1600; IT CONNECTS THE PRISON & THE DOGE'S PALACE	**$200**	WHAT IS
DOGE ENRICO DANDOLO ISSUED THESE, CALLED GROSSOS, WITH HIS PICTURE ON THEM	**$400**	WHAT ARE
14th CENTURY DOGE MARINO FALIERO WAS THE SUBJECT OF A TRAGEDY BY THIS "DON JUAN" POET	**$600**	WHO IS
SIMONE BOCCANEGRA WAS THE FIRST DOGE OF THIS CITY, HOME TO COLUMBUS	**$800**	WHAT IS
THIS CATHEDRAL IN VENICE WAS ORIGINALLY A PRIVATE CHAPEL OF THE DOGES	**$1000**	WHAT IS

DOUBLE JEOPARDY!

GOING TO THE DOGE

$200 — WHAT IS THE BRIDGE OF SIGHS? — **$200**

$400 — WHAT ARE (SILVER) COINS? — **$400**

$600 — WHO IS LORD BYRON? — **$600**

$800 — WHAT IS GENOA? — **$800**

$1000 — WHAT IS SAINT MARK'S CATHEDRAL? — **$1000**

DOUBLE JEOPARDY!

WEDDINGS

Clue	Value	Response
FOR A VEGAS CERE-MONY, YOU MAY WANT SOMEONE DRESSED AS THIS MAN WHO SANG "WEAR MY RING AROUND YOUR NECK"	**$200**	WHO IS
IN A PROTESTANT WEDDING CEREMONY, IT'S THE ROLE OF THE FATHER OF THE BRIDE	**$400**	WHAT IS
LUKE & LAURA'S 1981 TV WEDDING WAS CRASHED BY HELENA CASSADINE, PLAYED BY THIS SUPERSTAR	**$600**	WHO IS
THE 2-MONTH SALARY BENCHMARK FOR A RING-BUYING BUDGET WAS SET BY THIS DIAMOND MINING COMPANY IN THE 1980s	**$800**	WHAT IS
BORN IN 1809, THIS GERMAN COMPOSER WAS 17 WHEN HE BEGAN WORK ON HIS "WEDDING MARCH"	**$1000**	WHO IS

DOUBLE JEOPARDY!

WEDDINGS

$200	WHO IS ELVIS PRESLEY?	**$200**
$400	WHAT IS TO GIVE THE BRIDE AWAY?	**$400**
$600	WHO IS ELIZABETH TAYLOR?	**$600**
$800	WHAT IS DE BEERS?	**$800**
$1000	WHO IS FELIX MENDELSSOHN?	**$1000**

DOUBLE JEOPARDY!

SAY CHEESE!

HIS "POOR RICHARD'S ALMANAC" SAYS THAT "CHEESE AND SALT MEAT SHOULD BE SPARINGLY EAT"	**$200**	WHO IS
"MANY'S THE LONG NIGHT I'VE DREAMED OF CHEESE—TOASTED, MOSTLY", THIS AUTHOR WROTE IN "TREASURE ISLAND"	**$400**	WHO IS
THIS FRENCH PRESIDENT ASKED HOW ONE COULD BE EXPECTED TO GOVERN A COUNTRY THAT HAS "265 KINDS OF CHEESE?"	**$600**	WHO IS
THIS BROWNING WORK SAYS, "RATS! THEY FOUGHT THE DOGS AND KILLED THE CATS . . . AND ATE THE CHEESES OUT OF THE VATS"	**$800**	WHAT IS
IN HIS INTRODUCTION TO "A TALE OF A TUB", THIS IRISH-BORN SATIRIST SAYS THAT WISDOM "IS A CHEESE"	**$1000**	WHO IS

DOUBLE JEOPARDY!

SAY CHEESE!

$200	WHO IS BENJAMIN FRANKLIN?	**$200**
$400	WHO IS ROBERT LOUIS STEVENSON?	**$400**
$600	WHO IS CHARLES DE GAULLE?	**$600**
$800	WHAT IS "THE PIED PIPER (OF HAMELIN)"?	**$800**
$1000	WHO IS JONATHAN SWIFT?	**$1000**

DOUBLE JEOPARDY!

THEY REST IN RHODE ISLAND

Clue	Value	Response
SWAN POINT CEMETERY IS HOME TO ELISHA HUNT RHODES, WHOSE DIARY KEN BURNS USED IN A SHOW ON THIS SUBJECT	$200	WHAT IS
NICHOLAS COLASANTO, WHO WAS BEHIND THE BAR AS COACH ON THIS SITCOM, IS IN A CRANSTON, R.I. CEMETERY	$400	WHAT IS
LAST NAME OF THE 2 NAVAL BROTHERS, OLIVER & MATTHEW, WHO LIE IN ISLAND CEMETERY	$600	WHAT IS
THIS FOUNDER OF RHODE ISLAND HAS HIS OWN MEMORIAL IN PROVIDENCE	$800	WHO IS
THIS WRITER WHO CREATED CTHULHU WAS BORN, BRED & BURIED IN RHODE ISLAND	$1000	WHO IS

DOUBLE JEOPARDY!

THEY REST IN RHODE ISLAND

$200   WHAT IS THE CIVIL WAR?   **$200**

$400   WHAT IS "CHEERS"?   **$400**

$600   WHAT IS PERRY?   **$600**

$800   WHO IS ROGER WILLIAMS?   **$800**

$1000   WHO IS H.P. LOVECRAFT?   **$1000**

STATUES

ITS FACE WAS MODELED ON THE FEATURES OF AUGUSTE-CHARLOTTE BARTHOLDI

WHAT IS

FINAL JEOPARDY!

STATUES

WHAT IS THE
STATUE OF LIBERTY?

JEOPARDY!

NAME THE DECADE

PAUL REVERE TAKES A MIDNIGHT RIDE & WARNS THAT "THE BRITISH ARE COMING"	$100	WHAT ARE
WALTER MONDALE IS NOMINATED FOR PRESIDENT OF THE UNITED STATES	$200	WHAT ARE
THE 19th AMENDMENT IS RATIFIED; WOMEN CAN NOW VOTE!	$300	WHAT ARE
GOOD HEAVENS! ASTRONOMER CLYDE TOMBAUGH DISCOVERS PLUTO	$400	WHAT ARE
THE MAINE MYSTERI-OUSLY BLOWS UP IN HAVANA HARBOR	$500	WHAT ARE

JEOPARDY!

NAME THE DECADE

$100   WHAT ARE THE 1770s?   **$100**

$200   WHAT ARE THE 1980s?   **$200**

$300   WHAT ARE THE 1920s?   **$300**

$400   WHAT ARE THE 1930s?   **$400**

$500   WHAT ARE THE 1890s?   **$500**

JEOPARDY!

CINCINNATI

CINCINNATI'S ORIGINAL FOOTBALL TEAM CALLED THIS DIDN'T GET ITS NAME FROM THE TIGER, BUT FROM SOLDIERS IN INDIA	**$100**	WHAT ARE
THE SCULPTURE "GENIUS OF WATER" CROWNS ONE OF THESE STRUCTURES AT THE HEART OF CINCINNATI'S DOWNTOWN	**$200**	WHAT IS
AT OKTOBERFEST 1994, 48,000 CINCINNATIANS FLAPPED THEIR ELBOWS LIKE WINGS IN THIS DANCE	**$300**	WHAT IS
THE CONVENTION CENTER IS NAMED FOR DR. ALBERT SABIN, BEST KNOWN FOR DEVELOPING THIS IN CINCI IN THE '50s	**$400**	WHAT IS
THE GREATER CINCINNATI AIRPORT IS ACTUALLY ACROSS THE OHIO RIVER IN THIS STATE	**$500**	WHAT IS

JEOPARDY!

CINCINNATI

$100 — WHAT ARE THE BENGALS? — **$100**

$200 — WHAT IS A FOUNTAIN? — **$200**

$300 — WHAT IS THE CHICKEN DANCE? — **$300**

$400 — WHAT IS (ORAL) POLIO VACCINE? — **$400**

$500 — WHAT IS KENTUCKY? — **$500**

JEOPARDY!

G.G.'s

SHE WAS ONLY IN HER 30s WHEN SHE RETIRED FROM FILM AFTER THE RELEASE OF "TWO-FACED WOMAN" IN 1941	**$100**	WHO IS
THIS COMPOSER'S "PORGY AND BESS" IS PERHAPS THE MOST POPULAR OPERA EVER WRITTEN BY AN AMERICAN	**$200**	WHO IS
HE PROVIDED LIVE COVERAGE OF THE SUMMER OLYMPICS FROM ATLANTA, WHILE BROTHER BRYANT COVERED EVENTS IN NAGANO	**$300**	WHO IS
HER DISCO HIT "I WILL SURVIVE" BECAME AN ANTHEM FOR MANY WOMEN & IS STILL POPULAR TODAY	**$400**	WHO IS
NORMAN MAILER WROTE ABOUT THE LIFE & DEATH OF THIS CONVICTED KILLER IN HIS BOOK "THE EXECUTIONER'S SONG"	**$500**	WHO IS

JEOPARDY!

G.G.'s

$100 — WHO IS GRETA GARBO? — $100

$200 — WHO IS GEORGE GERSHWIN? — $200

$300 — WHO IS GREG GUMBEL? — $300

$400 — WHO IS GLORIA GAYNOR? — $400

$500 — WHO IS GARY GILMORE? — $500

JEOPARDY!

ONE WORD MISSING

OH, TO BE IN ___, / NOW THAT APRIL'S THERE	**$100**	WHAT IS
HAD WE BUT ___ ENOUGH, AND TIME, / THIS COYNESS, LADY, WERE NO CRIME	**$200**	WHAT IS
AN ___ MAN'S THE NOBLEST WORK OF GOD	**$300**	WHAT IS
I SHOULD HAVE BEEN A PAIR OF RAGGED ___ / SCUTTLING ACROSS THE FLOORS OF SILENT SEAS	**$400**	WHAT IS
MADE WEAK BY TIME AND FATE, BUT STRONG IN WILL / TO STRIVE, TO SEEK, TO FIND AND NOT TO ___	**$500**	WHAT IS

JEOPARDY!

ONE WORD MISSING

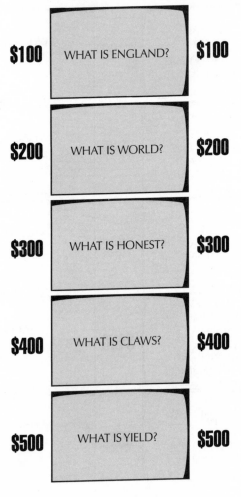

$100   WHAT IS ENGLAND? $100

$200   WHAT IS WORLD? $200

$300   WHAT IS HONEST? $300

$400   WHAT IS CLAWS? $400

$500   WHAT IS YIELD? $500

JEOPARDY!

HAIR CARE

Clue	Value	Response
A DAB OF PHYTO-SPECIFIC RELAXER MIGHT HAVE CONTROLLED THIS STANDOUT ON ALFALFA'S HEAD	$100	WHAT IS
THE BOBBY PIN WAS INTRODUCED IN THIS DECADE KNOWN FOR ITS BOBBED HAIR CRAZE	$200	WHAT ARE
IN 1954 THE "NO MORE TEARS" FORMULA OF THIS PRODUCT WAS INTRODUCED	$300	WHAT IS
AN ARCHIVE OF THIS SHAMPOO'S "GIRLS", INCLUDING BROOKE & CYBILL, IS HOUSED AT THE SMITHSONIAN	$400	WHAT IS
SALON HAIR CARE LINE HEADED & MODELED BY JOHN PAUL DeJORIA	$500	WHAT IS

JEOPARDY!

HAIR CARE

$100	WHAT IS A COWLICK?	**$100**
$200	WHAT ARE THE 1920s?	**$200**
$300	WHAT IS (JOHNSON &) JOHNSON'S BABY SHAMPOO?	**$300**
$400	WHAT IS BRECK?	**$400**
$500	WHAT IS PAUL MITCHELL?	**$500**

JEOPARDY!

CHILDREN'S LITERATURE

IN A FOLKTALE, THIS YUMMY "MAN" RUNS AWAY AFTER HE IS BAKED & IS LATER EATEN BY A SLY FOX	**$100**	WHO IS
MOWGLI IS THE MAIN CHARACTER OF THESE IMAGINATIVE RUDYARD KIPLING "BOOKS"	**$200**	WHAT ARE
IN THIS HANS CHRISTIAN ANDERSEN STORY, A CHILD OBSERVES, "HE HAS GOT NOTHING ON AT ALL!"	**$300**	WHAT IS
FERDINAND, THIS TYPE OF ANIMAL, JUST LIKES TO SIT & SMELL THE FLOWERS	**$400**	WHAT IS
IN A 1970 JUDY BLUME BOOK, THIS TITLE CHARACTER ASKED, "ARE YOU THERE GOD?"	**$500**	WHO IS

JEOPARDY!™

CHILDREN'S LITERATURE

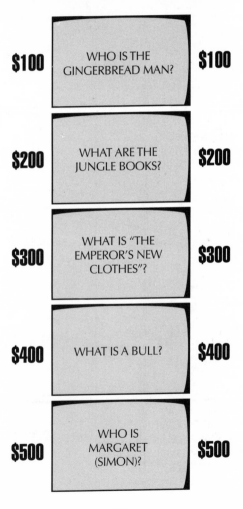

$100   WHO IS THE GINGERBREAD MAN?   **$100**

$200   WHAT ARE THE JUNGLE BOOKS?   **$200**

$300   WHAT IS "THE EMPEROR'S NEW CLOTHES"?   **$300**

$400   WHAT IS A BULL?   **$400**

$500   WHO IS MARGARET (SIMON)?   **$500**

DOUBLE JEOPARDY!

OSCAR-WINNING ROLES

HE WAS MORE THAN A CONTENDER AS THE BRAVE & SOMEWHAT DIM TERRY MALLOY	**$200**	WHO IS
HE WON FOR PLAYING A SUBURBAN DAD COMING TO LIFE IN "AMERICAN BEAUTY"	**$400**	WHO IS
BOXER PLAYED BY ROBERT DE NIRO IN "RAGING BULL"	**$600**	WHO IS
HE WON FOR PLAYING BLIND LT. COL. FRANK SLADE (RET.)	**$800**	WHO IS
GWYNETH PALTROW'S "SHAKESPEARE IN LOVE" CHARACTER SHARED THIS FIRST NAME WITH THE HEROINE OF "TWELFTH NIGHT"	**$1000**	WHAT IS

DOUBLE JEOPARDY!

OSCAR-WINNING ROLES

$200	WHO IS MARLON BRANDO?	**$200**
$400	WHO IS KEVIN SPACEY?	**$400**
$600	WHO IS JAKE LA MOTTA?	**$600**
$800	WHO IS AL PACINO?	**$800**
$1000	WHAT IS VIOLA?	**$1000**

DOUBLE JEOPARDY!

THE BLUE & THE GRAY

DANIEL HOUGH, THE CIVIL WAR'S FIRST FATALITY, DIED NOT IN BATTLE BUT IN AN ACCIDENT AT THIS FORT	**$200**	WHAT IS
THE SIEGE OF VICKS-BURG IN 1863 GAVE THE UNION CONTROL OF THIS RIVER	**$400**	WHAT IS
LESS THAN A MONTH AFTER GRADUATING LAST IN HIS CLASS FROM WEST POINT, HE MADE HIS FIRST STAND AT BULL RUN	**$600**	WHO IS
ROBERT E. LEE LOST NEARLY A QUARTER OF HIS TROOPS IN THIS MARYLAND BATTLE ALSO CALLED SHARPSBURG	**$800**	WHAT IS
THOUGH RELIEVED AS UNION ARMY CHIEF IN MARCH 1862, HE CON-TINUED TO LEAD THE ARMY OF THE POTOMAC UNTIL NOVEMBER	**$1000**	WHO IS

DOUBLE JEOPARDY!

THE BLUE & THE GRAY

$200	WHAT IS FORT SUMTER?	**$200**
$400	WHAT IS THE MISSISSIPPI?	**$400**
$600	WHO IS GEORGE CUSTER?	**$600**
$800	WHAT IS ANTIETAM?	**$800**
$1000	WHO IS GEORGE McCLELLAN?	**$1000**

DOUBLE JEOPARDY!

FASHION FOLKS

BEGUN IN 1913 & STILL IN OPERATION, THIS FASHION HOUSE "DE COCO" WAS CLOSED DOWN DURING WWII	**$200**	WHAT IS
THE MUCH TALKED-ABOUT FASHION DESIGN FIRM OF THIS MAN HAS BEEN HIS "OBSESSION" SINCE 1968	**$400**	WHO IS
THIS HIP DESIGNER FOR BOYS & "GIRL"S DESCRIBES THE AMERICAN STYLE OF HIS LINE AS "GOOD, CLEAN FUN"	**$600**	WHO IS
A FAMOUS REPTILIAN LOGO BELONGS TO THE DESIGN HOUSE BEGUN BY THIS TENNIS PLAYER	**$800**	WHO IS
AS SEEN ON RICHARD GERE IN "AMERICAN GIGOLO", SEXY SUITS FOR MEN WERE EARLY SUCCESSES FOR THIS FASHION LINE	**$1000**	WHAT IS

DOUBLE JEOPARDY!

FASHION FOLKS

$200	WHAT IS CHANEL?	**$200**
$400	WHO IS CALVIN KLEIN?	**$400**
$600	WHO IS TOMMY HILFIGER?	**$600**
$800	WHO IS RENE LACOSTE?	**$800**
$1000	WHAT IS ARMANI?	**$1000**

DOUBLE JEOPARDY!

"A" PLUS

FIRST NAME OF TV's McBEAL	$200	WHO IS
THIS WORD FOR A PAYMENT TO A FORMER SPOUSE IS FROM THE LATIN FOR "SUSTENANCE" OR "NOURISHMENT"	$400	WHAT IS
IN A 1992 SONG TITLE, IT DESCRIBES BILLY RAY CYRUS' HEART	$600	WHAT IS
A 2000 BOOK BY MOUNTAINEER REINHOLD MESSNER CLAIMS TO SOLVE THE MYSTERY OF THIS "SNOWMAN"	$800	WHAT IS
A CEREBRAL HEMORRHAGE, OR A FIT OF RAGE	$1000	WHAT IS

DOUBLE JEOPARDY!

"A" PLUS

$200	WHO IS ALLY?	$200
$400	WHAT IS ALIMONY?	$400
$600	WHAT IS ACHY BREAKY?	$600
$800	WHAT IS THE ABOMINABLE (SNOWMAN)?	$800
$1000	WHAT IS APOPLEXY?	$1000

DOUBLE JEOPARDY!

CHEMISTRY

YOU CAN ISOLATE ABOUT 1 GRAM OF THIS ELEMENT, Ra, OUT OF SEVERAL TONS OF PITCHBLENDE	**$200**	WHAT IS
IN THE 1700s GEORG ERNST STAHL COINED THE PHLOGISTON THEORY, THAT A FORM OF BURNING CAUSED THIS ON IRON	**$400**	WHAT IS
A FREE RADICAL IS AN ATOM OR MOLECULE THAT HAS AN ODD NUMBER OF THESE	**$600**	WHAT ARE
LITHIUM REACTS WITH THIS COMMON SUB-STANCE TO FORM LITHIUM HYDROXIDE	**$800**	WHAT IS
BROMINE & CHLORINE ARE IN A GROUP OF ELEMENTS KNOWN BY THIS NAME, FROM THE GREEK FOR "SALT-FORMING"	**$1000**	WHAT ARE

DOUBLE JEOPARDY!

CHEMISTRY

$200	WHAT IS RADIUM?	$200
$400	WHAT IS RUST?	$400
$600	WHAT ARE ELECTRONS?	$600
$800	WHAT IS WATER?	$800
$1000	WHAT ARE HALOGENS?	$1000

DOUBLE JEOPARDY!

BORN ON THE THIRD OF JULY

THIS "YANKEE DOODLE DANDY" COMPOSER WAS ACTUALLY BORN ON JULY 3 IN 1878	**$200**	WHO IS
"ROSENCRANTZ AND GUILDENSTERN ARE DEAD" IS A CLASSIC BY THIS JULY 3-BORN BRITISH PLAYWRIGHT	**$400**	WHO IS
BORN JULY 3, 1883 IN PRAGUE, THIS AUTHOR DIED AFTER A "TRIAL" WITH TB IN AN AUSTRIAN SANITARIUM JUNE 3, 1924	**$600**	WHO IS
BORN JULY 3, 1951, AT AGE 19 HE BECAME HAITI'S "PRESIDENT FOR LIFE"; WHY, HE WAS JUST A "BABY"	**$800**	WHO IS
ABOUT 200 YEARS BEFORE "JAWS", THIS AMERICAN PAINTER BORN JULY 3, 1738 PAINTED "WATSON AND THE SHARK"	**$1000**	WHO IS

DOUBLE JEOPARDY!

BORN ON THE THIRD OF JULY

$200	WHO IS GEORGE M. COHAN?	**$200**
$400	WHO IS TOM STOPPARD?	**$400**
$600	WHO IS FRANZ KAFKA?	**$600**
$800	WHO IS JEAN-CLAUDE "BABY DOC" DUVALIER?	**$800**
$1000	WHO IS JOHN SINGLETON COPLEY?	**$1000**

FINAL JEOPARDY!

CONTEMPORARY AMERICANS

THEY WERE THE 2 MAIN
FOUNDERS OF MICROSOFT

WHO ARE

FINAL JEOPARDY!

CONTEMPORARY AMERICANS

WHO ARE
BILL GATES & PAUL ALLEN?

JEOPARDY!

OFFICIAL STATE STUFF

THIS "FIRST STATE" HAS THE MOTTO "LIBERTY AND INDEPENDENCE"	**$100**	WHAT IS
THIS "CRAZY" CREATURE IS MINNESOTA'S STATE BIRD	**$200**	WHAT IS
THIS TREE THAT SOUNDS LIKE IT PRODUCES FABRIC IS WYOMING'S STATE TREE	**$300**	WHAT IS
MISSOURI'S STATE ONE OF THESE IS THE HAWTHORN	**$400**	WHAT IS
SOUTH DAKOTA'S STATE FISH IS THIS ONE THAT LOOKS AT YOU FUNNY	**$500**	WHAT IS

JEOPARDY!

OFFICIAL STATE STUFF

$100	WHAT IS DELAWARE?	**$100**
$200	WHAT IS THE LOON?	**$200**
$300	WHAT IS THE COTTONWOOD?	**$300**
$400	WHAT IS THE STATE FLOWER?	**$400**
$500	WHAT IS THE WALLEYE?	**$500**

JEOPARDY!

PIRATES

Clue	Value	Response
AMERICAN FORCES WON THIS JANUARY 1815 BATTLE WITH THE HELP OF PIRATES LED BY JEAN LAFFITE	**$100**	WHAT IS
A TYPE OF OLDSMOBILE SHARES ITS NAME WITH THIS KIND OF SWORD NO SELF-RESPECTING PIRATE WOULD BE WITHOUT	**$200**	WHAT IS
PIRATES OFFICIALLY LICENSED TO ATTACK ENEMY SHIPS DURING WARTIME WERE KNOWN BY THIS "SECRETIVE" NAME	**$300**	WHAT ARE
THIS "COLORFUL" PIRATE WAS PAID BY THE BRITISH TO ATTACK SPANISH SHIPS IN THE EARLY 1700s	**$400**	WHO IS
FROM THE FRENCH FOR "ONE WHO CURES MEAT", IT WAS A PIRATE WHO PREYED ON SPANISH SHIPPING IN THE WEST INDIES	**$500**	WHAT IS

JEOPARDY!

PIRATES

$100	WHAT IS THE BATTLE OF NEW ORLEANS?	$100
$200	WHAT IS A CUTLASS?	$200
$300	WHAT ARE PRIVATEERS?	$300
$400	WHO IS BLACKBEARD?	$400
$500	WHAT IS A BUCCANEER?	$500

JEOPARDY!

ENTERTAINING CANADIANS

LAST NAME OF CANADIAN-BORN ACTRESS MEG, JENNIFER'S SISTER	**$100**	WHAT IS
MOST KNOW WILLIAM SHATNER IS CANADIAN, BUT SO IS JAMES DOOHAN, WHO PLAYED THIS "STAR TREK" ENGINEER	**$200**	WHO IS
JOSHUA JACKSON, A STAR OF THIS MASSACHUSETTS-SET WB SERIES, IS A VANCOUVER NATIVE	**$300**	WHAT IS
ON SCREEN HE'S BEEN STUDIO 54 FOUNDER STEVE RUBELL & WOULD-BE WORLD DOMINATOR DR. EVIL	**$400**	WHO IS
IN 1970 THIS TORONTO-BORN NEWSMAN BEGAN HIS 3-DECADE CAREER AT "60 MINUTES"	**$500**	WHO IS

JEOPARDY!

ENTERTAINING CANADIANS

$100 WHAT IS TILLY? **$100**

$200 WHO IS SCOTTY? **$200**

$300 WHAT IS "DAWSON'S CREEK"? **$300**

$400 WHO IS MIKE MYERS? **$400**

$500 WHO IS MORLEY SAFER? **$500**

JEOPARDY!

WESTERN EUROPE

THE FRISIAN ISLANDS IN THIS SEA ARE DIVIDED AMONG GERMANY, DENMARK & THE NETHERLANDS	$100	WHAT IS
THIS 270-MILE MOUNTAIN CHAIN ONCE FORCED SPAIN & FRANCE TO TRADE BY SEA	$200	WHAT ARE
WE ASSUME THERE ARE ALSO PLENTY OF FEMALES ON THIS ISLE HALFWAY BETWEEN ENGLAND & IRELAND	$300	WHAT IS
DURING WWII THIS PALATIAL CITY SOUTH-WEST OF PARIS WAS THE SITE OF ALLIED GENERAL HEAD-QUARTERS	$400	WHAT IS
THE CELTIC SETTLEMENT LAUSONIUM, ON LAKE GENEVA, DEVELOPED INTO THIS SWISS CITY	$500	WHAT IS

JEOPARDY!

WESTERN EUROPE

$100 | WHAT IS THE NORTH SEA? | **$100**

$200 | WHAT ARE THE PYRENEES? | **$200**

$300 | WHAT IS THE ISLE OF MAN? | **$300**

$400 | WHAT IS VERSAILLES? | **$400**

$500 | WHAT IS LAUSANNE? | **$500**

JEOPARDY!™

DOUBLE-Z WORDS

Clue	Value	Response
A CHEAP, DILAPIDATED CAR, ESPECIALLY A MODEL T, IS REFERRED TO AS A TIN ONE OF THESE	$100	WHAT IS
IN THE TITLE OF A GOO GOO DOLLS ALBUM, IT PRECEDES "UP THE GIRL"	$200	WHAT IS
ON TV, IT'S THE BRAND OF BEER BREWED BY DREW CAREY & HIS FRIENDS	$300	WHAT IS
NICKNAME OF PRO GOLFER FRANK URBAN ZOELLER	$400	WHAT IS
INGRID BERGMAN STARRED IN THIS 1936 SWEDISH FILM AS WELL AS ITS HOLLYWOOD REMAKE 3 YEARS LATER	$500	WHAT IS

JEOPARDY!

DOUBLE-Z WORDS

$100   WHAT IS A LIZZIE?   **$100**

$200   WHAT IS DIZZY?   **$200**

$300   WHAT IS BUZZ?   **$300**

$400   WHAT IS FUZZY?   **$400**

$500   WHAT IS "INTERMEZZO"?   **$500**

JEOPARDY!

"TOM JONES"

Clue	Value	Response
IN BOOK 13 COUNTRY BOY TOM ARRIVES IN THIS METROPOLIS, WHERE THE CLIMACTIC ACTION TAKES PLACE	**$100**	WHAT IS
THIS AUTHOR OF THE NOVEL BASED THE HEROINE, SOPHIA, ON HIS BELOVED LATE WIFE	**$200**	WHO IS
TOM FINALLY LEARNS THE TRUE IDENTITY OF THIS PERSON; HE THOUGHT IT WAS JENNY THE MAID	**$300**	WHO IS
THE BENEVOLENT MR. ALLWORTHY & THE CRUDE MR. WESTERN HAVE THIS TITLE GIVEN TO ENGLISH COUNTRY GENTLEMEN	**$400**	WHAT IS
THIS "KUBLA KHAN" POET THOUGHT "TOM JONES" HAD 1 OF THE 3 BEST PLOTS IN ALL LITERATURE	**$500**	WHO IS

JEOPARDY!™

"TOM JONES"

$100 WHAT IS LONDON? $100

$200 WHO IS HENRY FIELDING? $200

$300 WHO IS HIS MOTHER? $300

$400 WHAT IS SQUIRE? $400

$500 WHO IS SAMUEL TAYLOR COLERIDGE? $500

DOUBLE JEOPARDY!

BODIES OF WATER

WINDERMERE IS THE LARGEST OF THESE IN THE ENGLISH "DISTRICT" NAMED FOR THEM	**$200**	WHAT IS
BAKU IN AZERBAIJAN & ASTRAKHAN IN RUSSIA ARE PORTS ON THIS STURGEON-FILLED SEA	**$400**	WHAT IS
A 1795 LAND FRAUD CASE CONCERNED LAND NEAR THE YAZOO, A TRIBUTARY OF THIS AMERICAN RIVER	**$600**	WHAT IS
THIS BAY SEPARATING NOVA SCOTIA & NEW BRUNSWICK HAS HIGH TIDES OF UP TO 70 FEET	**$800**	WHAT IS
THE WEDDELL SEA, BORDERING THIS CONTINENT, WAS NAMED FOR JAMES WEDDELL, WHO CHARTED IT IN 1823	**$1000**	WHAT IS

DOUBLE JEOPARDY!

BODIES OF WATER

$200	WHAT IS A LAKE?	**$200**
$400	WHAT IS THE CASPIAN SEA?	**$400**
$600	WHAT IS THE MISSISSIPPI?	**$600**
$800	WHAT IS THE BAY OF FUNDY?	**$800**
$1000	WHAT IS ANTARCTICA?	**$1000**

222

DOUBLE JEOPARDY!

LEGENDARY RHYME TIME

BUNYAN'S BARROOM FISTICUFFS	**$200**	WHAT ARE
ROBIN'S BOOTY THAT HE STOLE FROM THE RICH	**$400**	WHAT ARE
NORSE THUNDER GOD'S DAILY DUTIES	**$600**	WHAT ARE
LEGENDARY CARTHAGINIAN QUEEN'S FAITHFUL DOGS	**$800**	WHAT ARE
COUNTERPARTS OF GENTLEMEN IN THE GREEK UNDERWORLD	**$1000**	WHAT ARE

DOUBLE JEOPARDY!

LEGENDARY RHYME TIME

$200   WHAT ARE PAUL'S BRAWLS? $200

$400   WHAT ARE HOOD'S GOODS? $400

$600   WHAT ARE THOR'S CHORES? $600

$800   WHAT ARE DIDO'S FIDOS? $800

$1000   WHAT ARE HADES LADIES? $1000

DOUBLE JEOPARDY!

MOVIE ACTORS & ACTRESSES

Clue	Value	Response
JEAN MARSH OF "UPSTAIRS/DOWNSTAIRS" PLAYED ANTONY'S WIFE OCTAVIA IN THIS TAYLOR-&-BURTON EPIC	$200	WHAT IS
THIS TALLER HALF OF THE "GRUMPY OLD MEN" DUO PASSED AWAY IN 2000	$400	WHO IS
SHIRLEY EATON PLAYED THE GILDED GLAMOR GAL IN THIS 1964 SPY CLASSIC	$600	WHAT IS
ORIGINALLY NAMED SUSAN STOCKARD, SHE FOUND FAME & FORTUNE WHEN SHE CO-STARRED IN "THE FORTUNE" IN 1975	$800	WHO IS
THIS LEADING MAN OF "SPEED II" WAS FIRST SEEN ONSCREEN IN THE FUTURISTIC FLICK "SOLARBABIES"	$1000	WHO IS

DOUBLE JEOPARDY!

MOVIE ACTORS & ACTRESSES

$200 — WHAT IS "CLEOPATRA"? — $200

$400 — WHO IS WALTER MATTHAU? — $400

$600 — WHAT IS "GOLDFINGER"? — $600

$800 — WHO IS STOCKARD CHANNING? — $800

$1000 — WHO IS JASON PATRIC? — $1000

DOUBLE JEOPARDY!

THE 1930s

Clue	Value	Response
A 6-DAY FAST BY THIS MAN IN 1932 CHANGED THE WAY THE UNTOUCHABLES IN INDIA WERE TREATED	**$200**	WHO IS
THE FIRST FACTORY TO MAKE THESE CARS WAS DEDICATED IN WOLFSBURG, GERMANY MAY 26, 1938	**$400**	WHAT ARE
IN 1931 CHEMISTS DISCOVERED A GROWTH HORMONE IN THIS GLAND	**$600**	WHAT IS
POPE PIUS XI's "CASTI CONNUBII" ENCYCLICAL OF 1930 WAS LARGELY A CONDEMNATION OF THIS PRACTICE	**$800**	WHAT IS
TOPS IN COUNTRY MUSIC IN THE '30s WERE THIS FAMILY'S A.P., SARA & MAYBELLE	**$1000**	WHO IS

DOUBLE JEOPARDY!

THE 1930s

$200	WHO IS MAHATMA GANDHI?	$200
$400	WHAT ARE VOLKWAGENS?	$400
$600	WHAT IS THE PITUITARY GLAND?	$600
$800	WHAT IS BIRTH CONTROL?	$800
$1000	WHO IS THE CARTER FAMILY?	$1000

DOUBLE JEOPARDY!

SCIENCE

THIS OBJECT IN A SPECTROMETER SPREADS A BEAM OF LIGHT INTO SEPARATE COLORS	**$200**	WHAT IS
THE PART OF A TREE FROM WHICH QUININE & ASPIRIN'S SALICYLIC ACID ARE EXTRACTED	**$400**	WHAT IS
CROWBARS, NUTCRACKERS & ICE TONGS ARE DIFFERENT TYPES OF THIS SIMPLE MACHINE	**$600**	WHAT IS
THIS ORDER OF MAMMALS IS DIVIDED INTO PROSIMIANS & ANTHROPOIDS	**$800**	WHAT IS
IN A CHEMICAL PROCESS, MONOMERS, SMALL MOLECULES, LINK IN CHAINS TO FORM THESE LARGE MOLECULES	**$1000**	WHAT ARE

DOUBLE JEOPARDY!

SCIENCE

$200	WHAT IS A PRISM?	**$200**
$400	WHAT IS THE BARK?	**$400**
$600	WHAT IS A LEVER?	**$600**
$800	WHAT IS PRIMATES?	**$800**
$1000	WHAT ARE POLYMERS?	**$1000**

DOUBLE JEOPARDY!

CRYING

Clue	Value	Response
SHE WEPT IN 1998 WHEN PRESIDENT CLINTON AGREED TO SETTLE HER HARASSMENT LAWSUIT	$200	WHO IS
AS JIM BAKKER'S WIFE, THIS TELEVANGELIST WAS KNOWN FOR PUTTING ON MASCARA & SHEDDING TEARS	$400	WHO IS
IN 1961 JIMMY STEWART WEPT WHILE ACCEPTING AN OSCAR FOR THIS TERMINALLY ILL "HIGH NOON" STAR	$600	WHO IS
HIS APPARENT TEARS DURING A NEW HAMPSHIRE CAMPAIGN STOP DAMAGED HIS 1972 PRESIDENTIAL BID	$800	WHO IS
THE ANTI-POLLUTION COMMERCIAL IN WHICH AN INDIAN SHEDS ONE TEAR FEATURED ACTOR OSCAR CODY, NICKNAMED THIS	$1000	WHAT IS

DOUBLE JEOPARDY!

CRYING

$200	WHO IS PAULA JONES?	**$200**
$400	WHO IS TAMMY FAYE BAKKER?	**$400**
$600	WHO IS GARY COOPER?	**$600**
$800	WHO IS EDMUND S. MUSKIE?	**$800**
$1000	WHAT IS IRON EYES?	**$1000**

FINAL JEOPARDY!

U.S. GEOLOGY

THIS 800-MILE-LONG
FEATURE WAS DISCOVERED
& NAMED BY
ANDREW LAWSON

WHAT IS

FINAL JEOPARDY!
U.S. GEOLOGY

WHAT IS THE
SAN ANDREAS FAULT?

JEOPARDY!

CREEPERS & CRAWLERS

THE WORMLIKE LARVA OF A BUTTERFLY OR MOTH	**$100**	WHAT IS
WHEN REFERRING TO THE GLASS LIZARD, AUTOTOMY IS THE ABILITY TO DISCARD ALL OR PART OF THIS	**$200**	WHAT IS
THIS DARK LADY, LATRODECTUS MACTANS, EARNS HER MORE COMMON NAME BY KILLING & EATING HER MATE	**$300**	WHAT IS
THESE NOISEMAKERS CAN BE SIDEWINDERS OR DIAMONDBACKS	**$400**	WHAT ARE
FOUND ON INDONESIAN ISLANDS, THESE MONITORS ARE THE WORLD'S LARGEST LIVING LIZARDS	**$500**	WHAT ARE

JEOPARDY!

CREEPERS & CRAWLERS

$100	WHAT IS A CATERPILLAR?
$200	WHAT IS THE TAIL?
$300	WHAT IS THE BLACK WIDOW?
$400	WHAT ARE RATTLESNAKES?
$500	WHAT ARE KOMODO DRAGONS?

JEOPARDY!

U.S. MUSEUMS

WHEN DRIVING THROUGH SOUTH BEND IN THIS STATE, YOU CAN VISIT THE STUDEBAKER NATIONAL MUSEUM	**$100**	WHAT IS
WHEN YOU CARE ENOUGH TO VISIT THE VERY BEST, STOP BY THIS COMPANY'S VISITORS CENTER & MUSEUM IN KANSAS CITY	**$200**	WHAT IS
THIS CONFEDERATE TRAIN STOLEN DURING THE CIVIL WAR IS HOUSED AT GEORGIA'S BIG SHANTY MUSEUM	**$300**	WHAT IS
THE BUFFALO BILL MUSEUM IN THIS SMALL WYOMING CITY ALSO DISPLAYS ANNIE OAKLEY'S POSSESSIONS	**$400**	WHAT IS
ELIE WIESEL HELPED LIGHT AN ETERNAL FLAME AT THE 1993 DEDICATION OF THIS WASHINGTON, D.C. MUSEUM	**$500**	WHAT IS

JEOPARDY!

U.S. MUSEUMS

$100	WHAT IS INDIANA?	**$100**
$200	WHAT IS HALLMARK?	**$200**
$300	WHAT IS THE GENERAL?	**$300**
$400	WHAT IS CODY?	**$400**
$500	WHAT IS THE HOLOCAUST MEMORIAL MUSEUM?	**$500**

JEOPARDY!

"BIG" STUFF

Clue	Value	Response
IT THEORETICALLY HAPPENED ABOUT 10 TO 20 BILLION YEARS AGO	$100	WHAT IS
A MAN WITH MORE THAN ONE CURRENT MOTHER-IN-LAW	$200	WHAT IS
THIS HARDY SHEEP SHARES ITS NAME WITH A RIVER & A MOUNTAIN RANGE	$300	WHAT IS
GEORGE ORWELL'S OPPRESSIVE "SIBLING"	$400	WHO IS
A 1930 WALLACE BEERY MOVIE, OR SLANG FOR A PENITENTIARY	$500	WHAT IS

JEOPARDY!

"BIG" STUFF

$100 — WHAT IS THE BIG BANG? — $100

$200 — WHAT IS A BIGAMIST? — $200

$300 — WHAT IS THE BIGHORN? — $300

$400 — WHO IS BIG BROTHER? — $400

$500 — WHAT IS THE BIG HOUSE? — $500

JEOPARDY!

MOVIE QUOTES

Clue	Value	Response
1931 CHILLER THAT FEATURES "IT'S ALIVE! IT'S ALIVE!"	$100	WHAT IS
TITLE CHARACTER WHO SAYS, "PAY NO ATTENTION TO THAT MAN BEHIND THE CURTAIN"	$200	WHO IS
IN A 1967 FILM THIS ACTOR STERNLY INFORMS US THAT "THEY CALL ME MR. TIBBS!"	$300	WHO IS
IN "THE GRADUATE", "I JUST WANT TO SAY ONE WORD TO YOU— JUST ONE WORD . . ." THIS	$400	WHAT IS
DE NIRO-GRODIN PICTURE WITH THE MEMORABLE LINE "OF COURSE THEY'RE GAINING ON US! THEY'RE FLYING!"	$500	WHAT IS

JEOPARDY!

MOVIE QUOTES

$100	WHAT IS "FRANKENSTEIN"?	**$100**
$200	WHO IS THE WIZARD OF OZ?	**$200**
$300	WHO IS SIDNEY POITIER?	**$300**
$400	WHAT IS "PLASTICS"?	**$400**
$500	WHAT IS "MIDNIGHT RUN"?	**$500**

JEOPARDY!

KINGS & QUEENS

THIS BIBLICAL KING DID A BAD BAD THING WHEN HE IMPREGNATED BATHSHEBA	**$100**	WHO IS
OF THE 6 BRITISH KINGS WHO BORE THIS NAME, THE FIRST 4 WERE OF THE GERMAN HOUSE OF HANOVER	**$200**	WHAT IS
ABDULLAH BECAME KING OF THIS COUNTRY IN 1999, SUCCEEDING HIS FATHER, HUSSEIN	**$300**	WHAT IS
THIS HAWAIIAN KING WHOSE NAME MEANS "THE VERY LONELY ONE" CONQUERED MAUI IN 1790	**$400**	WHO IS
THIS KING OF CASTILE & ARAGON WAS KNOWN AS "THE CATHOLIC"	**$500**	WHO IS

JEOPARDY!

KINGS & QUEENS

$100	WHO IS KING DAVID?	$100
$200	WHAT IS GEORGE?	$200
$300	WHAT IS JORDAN?	$300
$400	WHO IS KAMEHAMEHA?	$400
$500	WHO IS FERDINAND (II OR V)?	$500

244

JEOPARDY!

IVANS

Clue	Value	Response
IN THIS DOSTOYEVSKY NOVEL, IVAN IS THE ATHEISTIC INTELLECTUAL OF THE 4 SONS	$100	WHAT IS
IVAN WAS THE MIDDLE NAME OF THIS ASTRONAUT, VIRGIL WAS HIS FIRST, BUT MOST PEOPLE CALLED HIM "GUS"	$200	WHO IS
AS DIRECTOR OF "TWINS" & "KINDERGARTEN COP", HE TOLD ARNOLD SCHWARZENEGGER WHAT TO DO	$300	WHO IS
IN A 1985 BOOK HE CALLED ARBITRAGE "WALL STREET'S BEST KEPT MONEY-MAKING SECRET"	$400	WHO IS
HE MUST HAVE SALIVATED OVER HIS JOB TEACHING PHYSIOLOGY AT THE INSTITUTE OF EXPERIMENTAL MEDICINE	$500	WHO IS

245

JEOPARDY!

IVANS

$100	WHAT IS "THE BROTHERS KARAMAZOV"?	**$100**
$200	WHO IS GUS GRISSOM?	**$200**
$300	WHO IS IVAN REITMAN?	**$300**
$400	WHO IS IVAN BOESKY?	**$400**
$500	WHO IS IVAN PAVLOV?	**$500**

DOUBLE JEOPARDY!

PRESIDENTIAL NICKNAMES

SUCCEEDING "TRICKY DICK", HE WAS JUST PLAIN "JERRY"	**$200**	WHO IS
HE WAS "THE ATLAS OF AMERICA" AS WELL AS "FIRST IN WAR", ETC.	**$400**	WHO IS
"BIG BEN" WOULD HAVE BEEN NICE; EVEN "GENTLE BEN"; BUT NO, HE HAD TO BE "LITTLE BEN"	**$600**	WHO IS
THE 1844 ELECTION MADE HIM "THE FIRST DARK HORSE"	**$800**	WHO IS
THIS 19th CENTURY PRESIDENT MADE THE LADIES QUIVER AS "HANDSOME FRANK"	**$1000**	WHO IS

DOUBLE JEOPARDY!

PRESIDENTIAL NICKNAMES

$200	WHO IS GERALD FORD?	**$200**
$400	WHO IS GEORGE WASHINGTON?	**$400**
$600	WHO IS BENJAMIN HARRISON?	**$600**
$800	WHO IS JAMES K. POLK?	**$800**
$1000	WHO IS FRANKLIN PIERCE?	**$1000**

DOUBLE JEOPARDY!

LATIN

CITIUS, ALTIUS, FORTIUS—SWIFTER, HIGHER, STRONGER—IS THE MOTTO OF THIS EVENT	**$200**	WHAT ARE
USED AS A FOOTNOTE ABBREVIATION, THIS WORD MEANS "IN THE SAME PLACE"	**$400**	WHAT IS
DESCARTES' "JE PENSE, DONC JE SUIS" IS BETTER KNOWN AS THIS LATIN PHRASE	**$600**	WHAT IS
IT'S THE ENGLISH TRANSLATION OF "ARS GRATIA ARTIS", THE MOTTO OF MGM	**$800**	WHAT IS
IN "THE SILENCE OF THE LAMBS" HANNIBAL LECTER BARGAINS WITH CLARICE USING THIS PHRASE MEANING "WHAT FOR WHAT"	**$1000**	WHAT IS

DOUBLE JEOPARDY!

LATIN

$200 — WHAT ARE THE OLYMPIC GAMES? — $200

$400 — WHAT IS IBID(EM)? — $400

$600 — WHAT IS COGITO ERGO SUM? — $600

$800 — WHAT IS "ART FOR ART'S SAKE"? — $800

$1000 — WHAT IS QUID PRO QUO? — $1000

DOUBLE JEOPARDY!

POP MUSIC

Clue	Value	Response
AMONG THE THEMES HE COMPOSED FOR BLAKE EDWARDS WERE "PETER GUNN" & "THE PINK PANTHER"	$200	WHO IS
HIS BACKUP BAND IS THE BUCKAROOS	$400	WHO IS
THE 1998 ALBUM "PAINTED FROM MEMORY" PAIRED THIS COMPOSER & ELVIS COSTELLO	$600	WHO IS
SHE COVERED "(I CAN'T GET NO) SATISFACTION" ON HER ALBUM "OOPS! . . . I DID IT AGAIN"	$800	WHO IS
VERONICA BENNETT FRONTED THIS "BE MY BABY" GROUP	$1000	WHAT IS

DOUBLE JEOPARDY!

POP MUSIC

$200	WHO IS HENRY MANCINI?	**$200**
$400	WHO IS BUCK OWENS?	**$400**
$600	WHO IS BURT BACHARACH?	**$600**
$800	WHO IS BRITNEY SPEARS?	**$800**
$1000	WHAT IS THE RONETTES?	**$1000**

252

DOUBLE JEOPARDY!

ICELAND COMETH

LOCATED ON FAXA BAY, IT WAS MADE THE CAPITAL OF ICELAND IN 1918	**$200**	WHAT IS
ICELAND'S NEAREST NEIGHBOR IS THIS ISLAND, ABOUT 190 MILES TO THE NORTHWEST	**$400**	WHAT IS
ICELAND WAS THE SITE OF ARMS CONTROL TALKS BETWEEN THESE 2 WORLD LEADERS IN OCTOBER 1986	**$600**	WHO ARE
96% OF THE POP-ULATION IS AFFILIATED WITH THE CHURCH OF ICELAND, WHICH IS THE EVANGELICAL TYPE OF THIS RELIGION	**$800**	WHAT IS
IN 1944 ICELAND GAINED FULL INDEPENDENCE FROM THIS PENINSULAR EUROPEAN COUNTRY	**$1000**	WHAT IS

DOUBLE JEOPARDY!

ICELAND COMETH

$200	WHAT IS REYKJAVIK?	**$200**
$400	WHAT IS GREENLAND?	**$400**
$600	WHO ARE RONALD REAGAN & MIKHAIL GORBACHEV?	**$600**
$800	WHAT IS LUTHERAN?	**$800**
$1000	WHAT IS DENMARK?	**$1000**

DOUBLE JEOPARDY!

BETTER MOUSETRAPS

Clue	Value	Response
THIS SWIMSUIT MADE ITS DEBUT SHORTLY AFTER THE APPEARANCE OF A MUSHROOM CLOUD OVER THIS PACIFIC ATOLL	**$200**	WHAT IS
KEEP YOUR COFFEE WARM IN ONE OF THESE BOTTLES INVENTED BY SIR JAMES DEWAR IN 1892	**$400**	WHAT IS
ARTHUR FRY DEVELOPED THIS PRODUCT FOR 3M AFTER TRYING TO BETTER MARK PAGES IN HIS HYMNAL	**$600**	WHAT ARE
SURE HOPE THIS GUY DIDN'T "BLIMP" UP WHILE CELEBRATING HIS INVENTION OF VULCANIZED RUBBER	**$800**	WHO IS
THIS BLACKSMITH IMPROVED THE PLOW IN THE LATE 1830s BY BUILDING THE FIRST ONE OF STEEL	**$1000**	WHO IS

DOUBLE JEOPARDY!

BETTER MOUSETRAPS

$200   WHAT IS BIKINI?   **$200**

$400   WHAT IS A THERMOS?   **$400**

$600   WHAT ARE POST-IT NOTES?   **$600**

$800   WHO IS CHARLES GOODYEAR?   **$800**

$1000   WHO IS JOHN DEERE?   **$1000**

DOUBLE JEOPARDY!

NAMES WE KNOW

THE LEADER OF ROCK & ROLL'S FAMILY STONE	**$200**	WHO IS
THIS 18-YEAR-OLD, A HERO IN THE FIGHT AGAINST AIDS, DIED IN INDIANA IN APRIL 1990	**$400**	WHO IS
THIS BRILLIANT ACTRESS, OSCAR-NOMINATED FOR "BEING JOHN MALKOVICH", IS MARRIED TO ACTOR DERMOT MULRONEY	**$600**	WHO IS
MUCH PHOTOGRAPHED IN 2000, MARISLEYSIS IS THE COUSIN OF THIS FAMOUS LITTLE CUBAN	**$800**	WHO IS
THIS FORMER HEAD OF THE URBAN LEAGUE & OF BILL CLINTON'S TRANSITION TEAM TESTIFIED ON TAPE FEB. 2, 1999	**$1000**	WHO IS

DOUBLE JEOPARDY!

NAMES WE KNOW

$200	WHO IS SLY (STONE)?	$200
$400	WHO IS RYAN WHITE?	$400
$600	WHO IS CATHERINE KEENER?	$600
$800	WHO IS ELIAN GONZALEZ?	$800
$1000	WHO IS VERNON JORDAN (JR.)?	$1000

FINAL JEOPARDY!

ENTERTAINMENT AWARDS

IN 1998 SHE BECAME
THE FIRST WOMAN
TO WIN AN OSCAR &
AN EMMY FOR LEAD
ACTRESS IN THE SAME YEAR

WHO IS

FINAL JEOPARDY!

ENTERTAINMENT AWARDS

WHO IS HELEN HUNT?

JEOPARDY!

FAMOUS NAMES

"LITTLE RED RIDING HOOD", A FILM HE ANIMATED IN 1922, WAS FOUND IN LONDON AROUND 20 YEARS AGO	$100	WHO IS
FAMOUS NICKNAME OF JOHN BIRKS GILLESPIE	$200	WHAT IS
THIS FAMOUS U-2 RECONNAISSANCE PILOT LATER BECAME A HELICOPTER TRAFFIC REPORTER	$300	WHO IS
THIS CARTOONIST FAMOUS FOR HIS "FAMILY" PUBLISHED "DRAWN AND QUARTERED" IN 1942	$400	WHO IS
HE SURPRISED MANY BY WITHDRAWING FROM THE 2000 NEW YORK SENATE RACE FOR PERSONAL REASONS	$500	WHO IS

JEOPARDY!

FAMOUS NAMES

$100	WHO IS WALT DISNEY?	**$100**
$200	WHAT IS DIZZY?	**$200**
$300	WHO IS FRANCIS GARY POWERS?	**$300**
$400	WHO IS CHARLES ADDAMS?	**$400**
$500	WHO IS RUDOLPH GIULIANI?	**$500**

JEOPARDY!

U.S. HISTORY

Clue	Value	Response
THE HOSTAGES HELD IN THIS COUNTRY WERE FREED MOMENTS AFTER REAGAN'S 1981 INAUGURATION	$100	WHAT IS
HER FIRST ATTEMPT TO FLY AROUND THE WORLD ENDED IN MARCH 1937 WHEN HER PLANE CRASHED IN HAWAII	$200	WHO IS
SAMUEL GOMPERS HELPED FOUND THE AMERICAN FEDERATION OF THIS	$300	WHAT IS
RUGGED-SOUNDING GROUP THAT STORMED SAN JUAN HILL ON JULY 1, 1898	$400	WHO ARE
IN 1952 CONGRESS APPROVED THIS COMMONWEALTH'S NEW CONSTITUTION	$500	WHAT IS

263

JEOPARDY!

U.S. HISTORY

$100 · WHAT IS IRAN? · $100

$200 · WHO IS AMELIA EARHART? · $200

$300 · WHAT IS LABOR? · $300

$400 · WHO ARE THE ROUGH RIDERS? · $400

$500 · WHAT IS PUERTO RICO? · $500

JEOPARDY!

NONPOTENT POTABLES

Clue	Value	Response
IN 1990 COCA-COLA INTRODUCED POWERADE TO COMPETE WITH THIS NO. 1-SELLING SPORTS DRINK	**$100**	WHAT IS
UNDER ITS MUG BRAND, PEPSICO MARKETS ROOT BEER & THIS DRINK FLAVORED WITH VANILLA	**$200**	WHAT IS
IN THE 1920s NATALI OLIVIERI HAD THE BRILLIANT IDEA OF FLAVORING YOO-HOO POP WITH THIS SWEET	**$300**	WHAT IS
THIS NORTHWEST CITY WAS A COFFEE MECCA PRE-WWII, LONG BEFORE STARBUCKS BEGAN THERE IN 1971	**$400**	WHAT IS
THIS SPARKLING LIQUID NAMED FOR A GERMAN TOWN WAS A FORE-RUNNER OF SODA POP	**$500**	WHAT IS

JEOPARDY!

NONPOTENT POTABLES

$100	WHAT IS GATORADE?	**$100**
$200	WHAT IS CREAM SODA?	**$200**
$300	WHAT IS CHOCOLATE?	**$300**
$400	WHAT IS SEATTLE?	**$400**
$500	WHAT IS SELTZER (WATER)?	**$500**

JEOPARDY!

"G" WHIZ!

Clue	Value	Response
IT'S A MERE STRIP OF GARMENT WORN BY STRIPPERS	$100	WHAT IS
IT'S THE CAUTIOUS WAY ASTAIRE MIGHT HAVE HELD ROGERS IF SHE WAS IN A BAD MOOD	$200	WHAT IS
IN THE EARLY '70s TITLEIST ENGINEERS DEVELOPED THE ICOSAHEDRON DIMPLE PATTERN FOR THESE	$300	WHAT ARE
TO "STRAIN AT" THIS INSECT "AND SWALLOW A CAMEL" MEANS TO FUSS OVER TRIFLES BUT IGNORE SERIOUS PROBLEMS	$400	WHAT IS
A PROFESSIONAL ERRAND-RUNNER, WHETHER OR NOT HE HAS CHEEK POUCHES	$500	WHAT IS

JEOPARDY!

"G" WHIZ!

$100 — WHAT IS A G-STRING? — **$100**

$200 — WHAT IS GINGERLY? — **$200**

$300 — WHAT ARE GOLF BALLS? — **$300**

$400 — WHAT IS A GNAT? — **$400**

$500 — WHAT IS A GOFER? — **$500**

268

JEOPARDY!

MASTERPIECES OF ART

Clue	Value	Response
GILBERT STUART'S UNFINISHED "ATHENAEUM HEAD" PORTRAIT OF THIS MAN APPEARS ON THE $1 BILL	$100	WHO IS
THIS SPANIARD'S "WEEPING WOMAN" IS THOUGHT TO BE MODELED ON HIS MISTRESS, DORA MAAR	$200	WHO IS
A FAMOUS 1793 PAINTING BY JACQUES-LOUIS DAVID DEPICTS THIS ASSASSINATED FRENCHMAN IN HIS BATHTUB	$300	WHO IS
HIS "YELLOW CHRIST" DATES FROM 1889, BEFORE HE LEFT FOR THE PAGAN SOUTH SEAS	$400	WHO IS
BORN IN 1599, THIS STUDENT OF RUBENS IS FAMOUS FOR HIS PORTRAIT OF MARCHESA ELENA GRIMALDI AS WELL AS OF KINGS	$500	WHO IS

JEOPARDY!

MASTERPIECES OF ART

$100 | WHO IS GEORGE WASHINGTON? | **$100**

$200 | WHO IS PABLO PICASSO? | **$200**

$300 | WHO IS JEAN PAUL MARAT? | **$300**

$400 | WHO IS PAUL GAUGUIN? | **$400**

$500 | WHO IS ANTHONY VAN DYCK? | **$500**

JEOPARDY!

TV SHOWS

SUMMER OF 2000 HIT SET ON REMOTE PULAU TIGA	**$100**	WHAT IS
NANCY CARTWRIGHT IS OVER 30 YEARS OLDER THAN THIS ANIMATED SON OF MARGE SHE VOICES	**$200**	WHO IS
A MESSAGE LEFT ON THIS ACTOR'S MACHINE MIGHT SAY, "LOVED YOU AS JIM ROCKFORD!"	**$300**	WHO IS
IN 2000 THIS SHOW STARRING MS. BRENNEMAN TOOK ON THE CONTROVERSIAL ISSUE OF BABY-SHAKING	**$400**	WHAT IS
KEN HOWARD STARRED IN THIS SERIES ABOUT A WHITE BASKETBALL COACH AT A TOUGH INNER-CITY SCHOOL	**$500**	WHAT IS

JEOPARDY!

TV SHOWS

$100 — WHAT IS "SURVIVOR"? — $100

$200 — WHO IS BART SIMPSON? — $200

$300 — WHO IS JAMES GARNER? — $300

$400 — WHAT IS "JUDGING AMY"? — $400

$500 — WHAT IS "THE WHITE SHADOW"? — $500

DOUBLE JEOPARDY!

HOW TRAGIC

Clue	Value	Response
SKIING MISHAPS CLAIMED THE LIVES OF MICHAEL KENNEDY & THIS ENTERTAINER-TURNED-CONGRESSMAN	**$200**	WHO IS
THOUGH NEARBY, THE CALIFORNIAN NEVER HEARD THIS LINER'S DISTRESS CALL IN 1912; ITS RADIO OPERATOR WAS OFF DUTY	**$400**	WHAT IS
THIS SINGER LEFT US NOT IN A JET PLANE BUT IN A SMALL EXPERIMENTAL PLANE IN 1997	**$600**	WHO IS
THIS MAY 6, 1937 DISASTER WAS BROADCAST ON RADIO	**$800**	WHAT IS
THIS WRITER & WIFE OF A FAMOUS AUTHOR DIED IN A FIRE AT A MENTAL HOSPITAL IN 1948	**$1000**	WHO IS

DOUBLE JEOPARDY!

HOW TRAGIC

$200	WHO IS SONNY BONO?	$200
$400	WHAT IS THE TITANIC?	$400
$600	WHO IS JOHN DENVER?	$600
$800	WHAT IS THE HINDENBURG CRASH?	$800
$1000	WHO IS ZELDA FITZGERALD?	$1000

DOUBLE JEOPARDY!

FICTIONAL CHARACTERS

Clue	Value	Response
GET TOO CLOSE TO THIS BELOVED FEMME & QUASIMODO JUST MIGHT RING YOUR BELL	**$200**	WHO IS
HE & HIS DOG WOLF WERE HUNTING SQUIRRELS IN THE CATSKILLS WHEN HE FELL ASLEEP	**$400**	WHO IS
LAST NAME OF SOAMES & IRENE, THE 2 PRINCIPAL CHARACTERS IN JOHN GALSWORTHY'S 3-NOVEL "SAGA"	**$600**	WHAT IS
ROXANE MARRIED CHRISTIAN DE NEUVILLETTE NOT KNOWING HIS LOVE LETTERS WERE WRITTEN BY THIS POET & SOLDIER	**$800**	WHO IS
IN THIS THACKERAY WORK, SIR PITT PROPOSES TO BECKY BUT SHE'S ALREADY SECRETLY MARRIED TO HIS SON RAWDON	**$1000**	WHAT IS

DOUBLE JEOPARDY!
FICTIONAL CHARACTERS

$200   WHO IS ESMERALDA?   **$200**

$400   WHO IS RIP VAN WINKLE?   **$400**

$600   WHAT IS FORSYTE?   **$600**

$800   WHO IS CYRANO DE BERGERAC?   **$800**

$1000   WHAT IS "VANITY FAIR"?   **$1000**

DOUBLE JEOPARDY!

KING CHARLES

Clue	Value	Response
A HOLIDAY IS NAMED FOR THIS BUILDING CHARLES V ADDED TO THE FORTIFICATIONS OF PARIS	**$200**	WHAT IS
ENGLAND'S CHARLES I DISMISSED IT IN 1629, RULED WITHOUT IT FOR 11 YEARS, THEN CALLED A SHORT ONE	**$400**	WHAT IS
HOLY ROMAN EMPEROR CHARLES II WAS NICKNAMED THIS; WE GUESS HE WASN'T THE HAIR APPARENT TO THE THRONE	**$600**	WHAT IS
THIS WOMAN WAS INSTRUMENTAL IN PUTTING THE DAUPHIN ON THE THRONE OF FRANCE AS KING CHARLES VII	**$800**	WHO IS
CHARLES III OF SPAIN MADE RELIGIOUS NEWS BY CURBING THIS INSTITUTION & EXPELLING THE JESUITS	**$1000**	WHAT IS

DOUBLE JEOPARDY!

KING CHARLES

$200	WHAT IS THE BASTILLE?	**$200**
$400	WHAT IS PARLIAMENT?	**$400**
$600	WHAT IS THE BALD?	**$600**
$800	WHO IS JOAN OF ARC?	**$800**
$1000	WHAT IS THE INQUISITION?	**$1000**

DOUBLE JEOPARDY!

THE SHORT VERSION

Clue	Value	Response
IN A COURTROOM, IT'S WHAT D.A. STANDS FOR	**$200**	WHAT IS
IN A LETTER, THIS ABBREVIATION PRECEDES AN AFTERTHOUGHT	**$400**	WHAT IS
BMW IS SHORT FOR THIS CAR COMPANY	**$600**	WHAT IS
LASER IS AN ACRONYM FOR LIGHT AMPLIFICATION BY STIMULATED EMISSION OF THIS	**$800**	WHAT IS
IN MEDICINE, HIV STANDS FOR THIS	**$1000**	WHAT IS

DOUBLE JEOPARDY!

THE SHORT VERSION

$200 — WHAT IS DISTRICT ATTORNEY? — $200

$400 — WHAT IS P.S.? — $400

$600 — WHAT IS BAVARIAN MOTOR WORKS? — $600

$800 — WHAT IS RADIATION? — $800

$1000 — WHAT IS HUMAN IMMUNODEFICIENCY VIRUS? — $1000

DOUBLE JEOPARDY!

BRITISH ACTRESSES

IN 1998 CLAIRE FORLANI GOT TO "MEET" THIS TITLE CHARACTER PLAYED BY BRAD PITT	$200	WHO IS
"SENSE AND SENSIBILITY" STAR WHO HAD A LONG PERSONAL & PROFESSIONAL PARTNERSHIP WITH KENNETH BRANAGH	$400	WHO IS
HELENA BONHAM CARTER USED A YANK ACCENT TO PLAY THIS MAN'S WIFE IN "MIGHTY APHRODITE"	$600	WHO IS
IN THE LATE '70s SHE STARRED AS FONTAINE KHALED IN "THE STUD", BASED ON A NOVEL BY HER SISTER	$800	WHO IS
FIRST NAME OF NATASHA RICHARDSON'S SISTER, SEEN IN 2000 IN "THE PATRIOT"	$1000	WHAT IS

DOUBLE JEOPARDY!

BRITISH ACTRESSES

$200	WHO IS JOE BLACK?	**$200**
$400	WHO IS EMMA THOMPSON?	**$400**
$600	WHO IS WOODY ALLEN?	**$600**
$800	WHO IS JOAN COLLINS?	**$800**
$1000	WHAT IS JOELY?	**$1000**

DOUBLE JEOPARDY!

ON THE ROAD

Clue	Value	Response
THE NATIONAL ARCHIVES EXHIBITION HALL IS ON THIS AVENUE, ALSO THE NAME OF A DOCUMENT HOUSED THERE	**$200**	WHAT IS
IT'S A MARTIN MILNER TV SHOW AS WELL AS A HISTORIC HIGHWAY	**$400**	WHAT IS
"THE STRIP", WHERE YOU'LL FIND CAESARS PALACE & THE MIRAGE, IS PROPERLY NAMED THIS BOULEVARD	**$600**	WHAT IS
YOU'LL FIND CLUBS LIKE THE WHISKY ON THE "STRIP" PART OF THIS L.A. BOULEVARD	**$800**	WHAT IS
THIS GLAMOROUS 1.18-MILE-LONG FRENCH STREET ENDING AT THE OBELISK OF LUXOR ALSO BOASTS A McDONALD'S	**$1000**	WHAT IS

DOUBLE JEOPARDY!

ON THE ROAD

$200 | WHAT IS CONSTITUTION AVENUE? | **$200**

$400 | WHAT IS ROUTE 66? | **$400**

$600 | WHAT IS LAS VEGAS (BOULEVARD)? | **$600**

$800 | WHAT IS SUNSET (BOULEVARD)? | **$800**

$1000 | WHAT IS THE CHAMPS-ELYSEES? | **$1000**

FINAL JEOPARDY!
CABLE TV

SPAWNING A WEB SITE, VIDEOS & A MAGAZINE, THIS A&E SERIES ONCE HOSTED BY PETER GRAVES TOOK ON A LIFE OF ITS OWN

WHAT IS

FINAL JEOPARDY!

CABLE TV

WHAT IS
"BIOGRAPHY"?

JEOPARDY!

17th CENTURY AMERICA

IN 1609 THIS SETTLE-MENT HAD ABOUT 500 PEOPLE, BUT DISEASE & STARVATION CUT THE NUMBER TO 60 BY SPRING 1610	**$100**	WHAT IS
IN 1614 THIS HUSBAND OF POCAHONTAS SENT THE FIRST EXPORT CARGO OF TOBACCO TO ENGLAND	**$200**	WHO IS
IN 1635 THE PUBLIC LATIN SCHOOL, THE FIRST PUBLIC SCHOOL IN BRITISH AMERICA, WAS ESTABLISHED IN THIS CITY	**$300**	WHAT IS
ON JANUARY 5, 1665 THE NEW HAVEN COLONY WAS FOR-MALLY ANNEXED BY THIS COLONY	**$400**	WHAT IS
ON APRIL 9, 1682 THIS FRENCHMAN REACHED THE MOUTH OF THE MISSISSIPPI RIVER & CLAIMED THE REGION	**$500**	WHO IS

JEOPARDY!

17th CENTURY AMERICA

$100	WHAT IS JAMESTOWN?	**$100**
$200	WHO IS JOHN ROLFE?	**$200**
$300	WHAT IS BOSTON?	**$300**
$400	WHAT IS CONNECTICUT?	**$400**
$500	WHO IS (SIEUR DE) LA SALLE?	**$500**

JEOPARDY!

AUTHORS

Clue	Value	Response
SAMUEL CLEMENS FIRST USED THIS PSEUDONYM ON FEBRUARY 3, 1863 IN VIRGINIA CITY'S TERRITORIAL ENTERPRISE	$100	WHAT IS
HIS "TROPIC OF CAPRICORN" WAS FIRST PUBLISHED IN FRANCE IN 1939; ITS U.S. RELEASE CAME 23 YEARS LATER	$200	WHO IS
IN 2000 HE WON AN OSCAR FOR ADAPTING HIS OWN NOVEL "THE CIDER HOUSE RULES"	$300	WHO IS
THE TOWN OF RED CLOUD, NEBRASKA HAS A HISTORICAL CENTER DEVOTED TO THIS AUTHOR	$400	WHO IS
IN 1999 THIS 84-YEAR-OLD AUTHOR OF "HUMBOLDT'S GIFT" & "MR. SAMMLER'S PLANET" BECAME A FATHER	$500	WHO IS

JEOPARDY!

AUTHORS

$100 — WHAT IS MARK TWAIN? — $100

$200 — WHO IS HENRY MILLER? — $200

$300 — WHO IS JOHN IRVING? — $300

$400 — WHO IS WILLA CATHER? — $400

$500 — WHO IS SAUL BELLOW? — $500

JEOPARDY!

BEAN COUNTING

TO MAKE THE POPULAR MEXICAN DISH FRIJOLES NEGROS, BEGIN WITH THESE BEANS	$100	WHAT ARE
IT'S THE BEAN WHOSE "MILK" IS USED TO MAKE TOFU	$200	WHAT IS
WHEN MAKING A HOMEMADE POT OF PORK & BEANS, YOU'LL BE AT SEA WITHOUT THESE BEANS	$300	WHAT ARE
LIKE CONTRACTS, RUNNER BEANS SHOULD HAVE NONE OF THESE ATTACHED; REMOVE THEM BEFORE COOKING	$400	WHAT ARE
THIS BEAN ENJOYED BY HANNIBAL LECTER IS ALSO KNOWN AS A BROAD BEAN	$500	WHAT IS

JEOPARDY!

BEAN COUNTING

$100   WHAT ARE BLACK BEANS? $100

$200   WHAT IS THE SOY BEAN? $200

$300   WHAT ARE NAVY BEANS? $300

$400   WHAT ARE STRINGS? $400

$500   WHAT IS A FAVA BEAN? $500

JEOPARDY!

ON THE "DOUBLE"

TWINS ADVERTISE THIS FLAVOR OF WRIGLEY'S GUM	**$100**	WHAT IS
IT'S SLANG FOR THE OLD 55-MILE-PER-HOUR NATIONAL SPEED LIMIT	**$200**	WHAT IS
THE FIFTH AMENDMENT PROTECTS AGAINST IT	**$300**	WHAT IS
A 1984 MELANIE GRIFFITH MOVIE, OR THE FUNCTION SHELLY MICHELLE SERVED FOR JULIA ROBERTS IN "PRETTY WOMAN"	**$400**	WHAT IS
"(JUST LIKE) STARTING OVER" IS ONE OF THE SONGS FROM THIS 1980 JOHN LENNON & YOKO ONO ALBUM	**$500**	WHAT IS

JEOPARDY!

ON THE "DOUBLE"

$100 — WHAT IS DOUBLEMINT? — $100

$200 — WHAT IS THE DOUBLE NICKEL? — $200

$300 — WHAT IS DOUBLE JEOPARDY? — $300

$400 — WHAT IS A BODY DOUBLE? — $400

$500 — WHAT IS "DOUBLE FANTASY"? — $500

JEOPARDY!™

BRITISH POP

"2 BECOME 1" & "WANNABE" WERE SMASH HITS FOR THIS FEMALE QUINTET	**$100**	WHAT IS
"GOD SAVE THE QUEEN" IS A CLASSIC BY THIS PUNK ROCK BAND, THE LEADERS OF THE SECOND BRITISH INVASION	**$200**	WHAT IS
THE 2 DAVIES BROTHERS WERE THE CORE OF THIS BRITISH GROUP	**$300**	WHAT IS
THIS BAND'S "BITTER SWEET SYMPHONY" RECYCLED A ROLLING STONES RIFF	**$400**	WHAT IS
WITH "TELSTAR", THIS BAND NAMED FOR A WEATHER PHENOM-ENON WAS THE FIRST BRITISH GROUP TO TOP THE U.S. CHARTS	**$500**	WHAT IS

JEOPARDY!

BRITISH POP

$100   WHAT IS THE SPICE GIRLS?   **$100**

$200   WHAT IS THE SEX PISTOLS?   **$200**

$300   WHAT IS THE KINKS?   **$300**

$400   WHAT IS THE VERVE?   **$400**

$500   WHAT IS THE TORNADOES?   **$500**

JEOPARDY!

PEOPLE & PLACES

A NEWCOMER TO THIS U.S. STATE IS KNOWN TO LOCALS AS A MALIHINI	$100	WHAT IS
PRESIDENTS OF TIBLISI & BATUMI, OR OF PLAINS & MACON	$200	WHAT ARE
A NATIVE OF FLANDERS, OR ICE SKATER PEGGY	$300	WHAT IS
BIGGER SWINGERS THAN MOST SOUTH AMERICANS, THE PEOPLE OF THIS CITY ARE CARAQUENOS	$400	WHAT IS
THE PEOPLE OF THIS BRITISH CITY ARE CALLED BRUMMIES, FROM BRUMMAGEM, AN OLD SLANG NAME FOR THE TOWN	$500	WHAT IS

JEOPARDY!

PEOPLE & PLACES

$100 — WHAT IS HAWAII? — **$100**

$200 — WHAT ARE GEORGIANS? — **$200**

$300 — WHAT IS A FLEMING? — **$300**

$400 — WHAT IS CARACAS? — **$400**

$500 — WHAT IS BIRMINGHAM? — **$500**

DOUBLE JEOPARDY!

SCIENCE & NATURE

THESE DARK PATCHES ON THE SUN'S SURFACE APPEAR & DISAPPEAR IN REGULAR CYCLES	$200	WHAT ARE
FROM THE GREEK FOR "YOKE", IT'S A CELL FORMED BY THE UNION OF 2 GAMETES	$400	WHAT IS
THIS "SEA" CREATURE IS A VASE-SHAPED POLYP WITH MOUSE SURROUNDED BY TENTACLES	$600	WHAT IS
SON OF A GUN! THIS FEMALE, SEED-BEARING PART OF A FLOWER CONSISTS OF A STIGMA, A STYLE & AN OVARY	$800	WHAT IS
ANNOUNCED ON FEBRUARY 14, 1946, THIS FIRST ELECTRONIC DIGITAL COMPUTER HAD 18,000 VACUUM TUBES	$1000	WHAT IS

DOUBLE JEOPARDY!

SCIENCE & NATURE

$200	WHAT ARE SUNSPOTS?	$200
$400	WHAT IS A ZYGOTE?	$400
$600	WHAT IS A SEA ANEMONE?	$600
$800	WHAT IS THE PISTIL?	$800
$1000	WHAT IS ENIAC?	$1000

300

DOUBLE JEOPARDY!

THAT'S HISTORY

FERDINAND & ISABELLA PROMISED TO MAKE HIM "ADMIRAL OF THE OCEAN SEA" IF HE WAS SUCCESSFUL IN HIS 1492 VOYAGE	**$200**	WHO IS
IN 1455 JOHANN FUST WON A JUDGMENT AGAINST THIS PRINTER & TOOK THE TYPE USED TO PRINT HIS FAMOUS BIBLE	**$400**	WHO IS
IN 1795 AUSTRIA, PRUSSIA & RUSSIA PARTITIONED THIS COUNTRY, ELIMINATING ITS EXISTENCE	**$600**	WHAT IS
AT THE DEATH OF CARDINAL MAZARIN IN 1661, THIS FRENCH KING DECLARED THAT HE WOULD SERVE AS HIS OWN PRIME MINISTER	**$800**	WHO IS
THIS ANCIENT NORTH AFRICAN CITY-STATE WAS PROTECTED BY A HIGH WALL ABOUT 23 MILES IN LENGTH	**$1000**	WHAT IS

DOUBLE JEOPARDY!

THAT'S HISTORY

$200
WHO IS CHRISTOPHER COLUMBUS?
$200

$400
WHO IS JOHANN(ES) GUTENBERG?
$400

$600
WHAT IS POLAND?
$600

$800
WHO IS LOUIS XIV?
$800

$1000
WHAT IS CARTHAGE?
$1000

DOUBLE JEOPARDY!

MUSKRAT LOVE

Clue	Value	Response
MUSKRAT FAMILIES OFTEN LIVE IN DENS CALLED THESE, LIKE THE HOMES OF BEAVERS & CERTAIN "ELKS"	$200	WHAT ARE
BECAUSE IT'S NATIVE TO THIS "SUNSHINE STATE", THE ROUND-TAILED MUSKRAT CAN BREED YEAR-ROUND	$400	WHAT IS
FROM LATIN FOR "BED", FEMALE MUSKRATS HAVE 2–5 OF THEM A YEAR WITH 5–7 YOUNG IN EACH	$600	WHAT IS
IN MUSKRATS THIS PERIOD, WHOSE NAME IS FROM LATIN FOR "CARRYING", LASTS LESS THAN A MONTH	$800	WHAT IS
IN BREEDING SEASON, 2 OF THESE ORGANS ENLARGE TO PRODUCE THE "MUSK" IN THE ANIMAL'S NAME	$1000	WHAT ARE

DOUBLE JEOPARDY!

MUSKRAT LOVE

$200	WHAT ARE LODGES?	**$200**
$400	WHAT IS FLORIDA?	**$400**
$600	WHAT IS A LITTER?	**$600**
$800	WHAT IS GESTATION?	**$800**
$1000	WHAT ARE GLANDS?	**$1000**

DOUBLE JEOPARDY!

ORGANIZATIONS

Clue	Value	Response
IN 1997 THIS ORGANIZATION CELEBRATED THE 90th ANNIVERSARY OF ITS CHRISTMAS SEALS	**$200**	WHAT IS
AN ADORABLE LITTLE PANDA IS THE SYMBOL OF THIS "FUND" FOUNDED IN 1961	**$400**	WHAT IS
IN 1997 MARTIN LUTHER KING III WAS ELECTED PRESIDENT OF THIS GROUP, THE SCLC; DAD WOULD HAVE BEEN PROUD	**$600**	WHAT IS
THE "WORLD" ONE OF THESE IS OFFICIALLY THE "INTERNATIONAL" ONE "FOR RECONSTRUCTION & DEVELOPMENT"	**$800**	WHAT IS
AN ASSOCIATION IN ANNANDALE, VIRGINIA IS DEVOTED TO THIS MAN, JEFFERSON'S VICE PRESIDENT & THE SUBJECT OF A MILK AD	**$1000**	WHO IS

DOUBLE JEOPARDY!

ORGANIZATIONS

$200 — WHAT IS THE AMERICAN LUNG ASSOCIATION? — $200

$400 — WHAT IS THE WORLD WILDLIFE FUND? — $400

$600 — WHAT IS THE SOUTHERN CHRISTIAN LEADERSHIP CONFERENCE? — $600

$800 — WHAT IS BANK? — $800

$1000 — WHO IS AARON BURR? — $1000

DOUBLE JEOPARDY!

TOUGH FOOTBALL

IN 1967 THIS NEW YORK JET BECAME THE FIRST NFL QUARTERBACK TO THROW FOR OVER 4,000 YARDS IN A SEASON	**$200**	WHO IS
RUNNING BACK THURMAN THOMAS OF THIS TEAM IS THE ONLY PLAYER TO SCORE IN 4 CONSECUTIVE SUPER BOWLS	**$400**	WHAT ARE
HE TOOK OVER AS THE VIKINGS' COACH IN 1992 & LED THEM THROUGH THE REST OF THE '90s	**$600**	WHO IS
IN 1998 HIS 1,846 RUSHING YARDS HELPED THE ATLANTA FALCONS GET TO THE SUPER BOWL	**$800**	WHO IS
ON NOV. 8, 1970 THIS MAN HELPED THE SAINTS BEAT THE LIONS BY KICKING A RECORD-SETTING 63-YARD FIELD GOAL	**$1000**	WHO IS

DOUBLE JEOPARDY!

TOUGH FOOTBALL

$200 WHO IS JOE NAMATH? **$200**

$400 WHAT ARE THE BUFFALO BILLS? **$400**

$600 WHO IS DENNIS GREEN? **$600**

$800 WHO IS JAMAL ANDERSON? **$800**

$1000 WHO IS TOM DEMPSEY? **$1000**

DOUBLE JEOPARDY!

WRONG!

Clue	Value	Response
FOLLOW A FALSE LEAD & YOU'RE DOING THIS "UP THE WRONG TREE"	**$200**	WHAT IS
A BADLY MISTAKEN BASEBALL PLAYER IS WAY "OFF" THIS, BE IT FIRST OR HOME	**$400**	WHAT IS
"A CASE OF" THIS MAY INVOLVE PICKING THE WRONG PERSON OUT OF A POLICE LINE-UP	**$600**	WHAT IS
TIPO, ER . . . TYPO IS SHORT FOR THIS 2-WORD PHRASE	**$800**	WHAT IS
FRENCH FOR "FALSE STEP"; YOU DON'T WANT TO COMMIT A SOCIAL ONE	**$1000**	WHAT IS

DOUBLE JEOPARDY!

WRONG!

$200   WHAT IS BARKING? $200

$400   WHAT IS BASE? $400

$600   WHAT IS MISTAKEN IDENTITY? $600

$800   WHAT IS TYPO-GRAPHICAL ERROR? $800

$1000   WHAT IS A FAUX PAS? $1000

FINAL JEOPARDY!
COUNTRIES

THIS ISLAND NATION IS
THE ONLY COUNTRY IN
THE WORLD NAMED FOR
A BIBLICAL KING

WHAT ARE

FINAL JEOPARDY!
COUNTRIES

WHAT ARE THE
SOLOMON ISLANDS?